MAD LIBS®

OFF-THE-WALL MAD LIBS

by Roger Price & Leonard Stern

PSS!

PRICE STERN SLOAN

An Imprint of Penguin Group (USA) Inc.

This 2012 custom edition is exclusively published for Barnes & Noble by Price Stern Sloan,
a division of Penguin Young Readers Group. ISBN 978-0-7607-7282-9

Special Markets ISBN: 978-0-8431-8913-1

15 14 13 12 11 10 9 8 7

PRICE STERN SLOAN

Penguin Group (USA) Inc., 375 Hudson Street, New York, New York 10014, USA
Penguin Group (Canada), 90 Eglinton Avenue East, Suite 700,
Toronto, Ontario M4P 2Y3, Canada (a division of Pearson Penguin Canada Inc.)
Penguin Books Ltd, 80 Strand, London WC2R 0RL, England
Penguin Ireland, 25 St Stephen's Green, Dublin 2, Ireland (a division of Penguin Books Ltd)
Penguin Group (Australia), 707 Collins Street, Melbourne, Victoria 3008, Australia
(a division of Pearson Australia Group Pty Ltd)
Penguin Books India Pvt Ltd, 11 Community Centre,
Panchsheel Park, New Delhi—110 017, India
Penguin Group (NZ), 67 Apollo Drive, Rosedale, Auckland 0632, New Zealand
(a division of Pearson New Zealand Ltd)
Penguin Books, Rosebank Office Park, 181 Jan Smuts Avenue,
Parktown North 2193, South Africa
Penguin China, B7 Jiaming Center, 27 East Third Ring Road North,
Chaoyang District, Beijing 100020, China

Penguin Books Ltd, Registered Offices:
80 Strand, London WC2R 0RL, England

Published by Price Stern Sloan, a division of Penguin Young Readers Group,
345 Hudson Street, New York, New York 10014.

ISBN 0-8431-0108-3

PSS! and MAD LIBS are registered trademarks of Penguin Group (USA) Inc.

MAD LIBS
INSTRUCTIONS

MAD LIBS® is a game for people who don't like games!
It can be played by one, two, three, four, or forty.

• RIDICULOUSLY SIMPLE DIRECTIONS

In this tablet you will find stories containing blank spaces where words are left out. One player, the READER, selects one of these stories. The READER does not tell anyone what the story is about. Instead, he/she asks the other players, the WRITERS, to give him/her words. These words are used to fill in the blank spaces in the story.

• TO PLAY

The READER asks each WRITER in turn to call out a word—an adjective or a noun or whatever the space calls for—and uses them to fill in the blank spaces in the story. The result is a MAD LIBS® game.

When the READER then reads the completed MAD LIBS® game to the other players, they will discover that they have written a story that is fantastic, screamingly funny, shocking, silly, crazy, or just plain dumb—depending upon which words each WRITER called out.

• EXAMPLE (*Before* and *After*)

"_____!" he said _____
         EXCLAMATION   ADVERB

as he jumped into his convertible _____ and
                                                    NOUN

drove off with his _____ wife.
                              ADJECTIVE

"_____*Ouch*_____!" he said _____*stupidly*_____
         EXCLAMATION   ADVERB

as he jumped into his convertible _____*cat*_____ and
                                                    NOUN

drove off with his _____*brave*_____ wife.
                              ADJECTIVE

MAD LIBS®
QUICK REVIEW

In case you have forgotten what adjectives, adverbs, nouns, and verbs are, here is a quick review:

An ADJECTIVE describes something or somebody. *Lumpy*, *soft*, *ugly*, *messy*, and *short* are adjectives.

An ADVERB tells how something is done. It modifies a verb and usually ends in "ly." *Modestly*, *stupidly*, *greedily*, and *carefully* are adverbs.

A NOUN is the name of a person, place, or thing. *Sidewalk*, *umbrella*, *bridle*, *bathtub*, and *nose* are nouns.

A VERB is an action word. *Run*, *pitch*, *jump*, and *swim* are verbs. Put the verbs in past tense if the directions say PAST TENSE. *Ran*, *pitched*, *jumped*, and *swam* are verbs in the past tense.

When we ask for A PLACE, we mean any sort of place: a country or city (*Spain*, *Cleveland*) or a room (*bathroom*, *kitchen*).

An EXCLAMATION or SILLY WORD is any sort of funny sound, gasp, grunt, or outcry, like *Wow!*, *Ouch!*, *Whomp!*, *Ick!*, and *Gadzooks!*

When we ask for specific words, like a NUMBER, a COLOR, an ANIMAL, or a PART OF THE BODY, we mean a word that is one of those things, like *seven*, *blue*, *horse*, or *head*.

When we ask for a PLURAL, it means more than one. For example, *cat* pluralized is *cats*.

MAD LIBS® is fun to play with friends, but you can also play it by yourself! To begin with, DO NOT look at the story on the page below. Fill in the blanks on this page with the words called for. Then, using the words you have selected, fill in the blank spaces in the story.

Now you've created your own hilarious MAD LIBS® game!

PAUL REVERE

STATE _____

ADJECTIVE _____

NOUN _____

NATIONALITY _____

NOUN _____

TYPE OF LIQUID _____

PLACE _____

NOUN _____

NOUN _____

NOUN _____

ADVERB _____

PLURAL NOUN _____

SAME PLURAL NOUN _____

CELEBRITY (MALE) _____

MAD LIBS®
PAUL REVERE

Paul Revere was born in Boston, _____ , in 1735.
STATE

His father taught him to work with metals, and he soon became a/an

_____ _____ . He was a soldier in the
ADJECTIVE   NOUN

French and _____ War and was at the famous Boston
NATIONALITY

_____ Party when Americans dressed as Indians dumped tons of
NOUN

_____ into the ocean. On April 18, 1775, Paul Revere
TYPE OF LIQUID

waited in _____ for a signal light from a church tower. The
PLACE

signal was to be one if by _____ , two if by _____ .
NOUN   NOUN

When he got the message, he mounted his faithful _____
NOUN

and rode off _____ . On the way, he kept yelling, "The
ADVERB

_____ are coming! The _____ are coming!"
PLURAL NOUN   SAME PLURAL NOUN

This was the beginning of the American War for Independence from

King _____ .
CELEBRITY (MALE)

MAD LIBS® is fun to play with friends, but you can also play it by yourself! To begin with, DO NOT look at the story on the page below. Fill in the blanks on this page with the words called for. Then, using the words you have selected, fill in the blank spaces in the story.

Now you've created your own hilarious MAD LIBS® game!

ELIZABETH THE FIRST

_____ NOUN

_____ ADJECTIVE (SUPERLATIVE)

_____ NOUN

_____ ADJECTIVE

_____ ADJECTIVE

_____ ADVERB

_____ NATIONALITY

_____ CELEBRITY

_____ ANOTHER CELEBRITY

_____ NAME OF PERSON

_____ ADJECTIVE

MAD☺LIBS

ELIZABETH THE FIRST

Elizabeth, the Tudor _____ of England, was probably the
                              NOUN

_____ ruler the British ever had. Elizabeth was the
ADJECTIVE (SUPERLATIVE)

daughter of Henry the Eighth and Anne Boleyn. Later, Anne had her

_____ chopped off by Henry.
      NOUN

Elizabeth was born in 1533 and became queen when she was 25. She

was a/an _____ Protestant and persecuted the _____
               ADJECTIVE   ADJECTIVE

Catholics _____ . In 1588, the _____ Armada
               ADVERB   NATIONALITY

attacked England. But the English fleet, commanded by _____
                                                              CELEBRITY

and _____ , defeated them. Elizabeth ruled for 45 years,
      ANOTHER CELEBRITY

and during her reign England prospered and produced Shakespeare,

Francis Bacon, and _____ . Elizabeth never married,
                        NAME OF PERSON

which is why she is sometimes called the _____ Queen.
                                                  ADJECTIVE

MAD LIBS® is fun to play with friends, but you can also play it by yourself! To begin with, DO NOT look at the story on the page below. Fill in the blanks on this page with the words called for. Then, using the words you have selected, fill in the blank spaces in the story.

Now you've created your own hilarious MAD LIBS® game!

REPORT BY STUDENT PROTEST COMMITTEE

SCHOOL _____

ADJECTIVE _____

PLURAL NOUN _____

PERSON IN ROOM (MALE) _____

PART OF THE BODY _____

ARTICLE OF CLOTHING _____

PLURAL NOUN _____

NOUN _____

NOUN _____

ADJECTIVE _____

ADJECTIVE _____

PLURAL NOUN _____

MAD LIBS®
REPORT BY STUDENT PROTEST COMMITTEE

Fellow students of _____ ! We the members of the Students
SCHOOL

for a/an _____ Society are meeting here to decide what
ADJECTIVE

action to take about the Dean of _____ . He has just fired
PLURAL NOUN

our friend, Professor _____ , because he wore his
PERSON IN ROOM (MALE)

_____ long, and because he dressed in a/an
PART OF THE BODY

_____ and wore old _____ . Next week,
ARTICLE OF CLOTHING   PLURAL NOUN

we are going to protest by taking over the _____
NOUN

building and kidnapping the Assistant _____ . We also
NOUN

will demand that all students have the right to wear _____
ADJECTIVE

hair and _____ beards. Remember our slogan:
ADJECTIVE

"Down with _____ ."
PLURAL NOUN

MAD LIBS® is fun to play with friends, but you can also play it by yourself! To begin with, DO NOT look at the story on the page below. Fill in the blanks on this page with the words called for. Then, using the words you have selected, fill in the blank spaces in the story.

Now you've created your own hilarious MAD LIBS® game!

ALEXANDER THE GREAT

NOUN_____

NOUN_____

CELEBRITY_____

NOUN_____

CELEBRITY_____

A PLACE_____

NOUN_____

SILLY WORD_____

PLURAL NOUN_____

TYPE OF LIQUID_____

PART OF THE BODY_____

PLURAL NOUN_____

MAD☺LIBS®
ALEXANDER THE GREAT

In 356 B.C., Phillip of Macedonia, the ruler of a province in northern

Greece, became the father of a bouncing baby _____
                                                    NOUN

named Alexander. Alexander's teacher was Aristotle, the famous

_____ .When he was 20 years old, his father was murdered
      NOUN

by _____ , after which he became _____ of all
        CELEBRITY   NOUN

Macedonia. In 334, he invaded Persia and defeated _____
                                                          CELEBRITY

at the Battle of _____ . Later, at Arbela, he won his most
                    A PLACE

important victory, over Darius the Third. This made him _____
                                                               NOUN

_____ over all Persians. Then he marched to India, and
   SILLY WORD

many of his _____ died. After that, Alexander began
                PLURAL NOUN

drinking too much _____ , and at the age of 33, he died
                      TYPE OF LIQUID

of an infection in the _____ . His last words are reported
                          PART OF THE BODY

to have been, "There are no more _____ to conquer."
                                      PLURAL NOUN

MAD LIBS® is fun to play with friends, but you can also play it by yourself! To begin with, DO NOT look at the story on the page below. Fill in the blanks on this page with the words called for. Then, using the words you have selected, fill in the blank spaces in the story.

Now you've created your own hilarious MAD LIBS® game!

EASTER

PLURAL NOUN _____

NUMBER _____

ADJECTIVE _____

NOUN _____

TYPE OF GAME _____

ADJECTIVE _____

PLURAL NOUN _____

ADJECTIVE _____

ADJECTIVE _____

TYPE OF LIQUID _____

NOUN _____

ANOTHER TYPE OF LIQUID _____

ADJECTIVE _____

Spring vacation usually falls around Easter time. The schools are

closed and all the _____ get _____ weeks off.
                        PLURAL NOUN   NUMBER

The _____ teachers also get a vacation. There are a lot of
      ADJECTIVE

things to do during Easter vacation. Some kids loaf around and

watch the _____. Others get outside and play _____,
            NOUN   TYPE OF GAME

while more ambitious students spend their time studying

their _____ books so they will grow up to become
        ADJECTIVE

_____. Little kids also color _____ eggs.
  PLURAL NOUN   ADJECTIVE

Here's how you color an egg: First, mix a package of _____
                                                       ADJECTIVE

dye in a bowl full of _____. Then, dip a/an _____
                        TYPE OF LIQUID   NOUN

in the bowl and rinse it off with _____. Then, after
                                   ANOTHER TYPE OF LIQUID

it dries, you can paint on it with a brush. Then you show it to your

friends, who will say, "Boy, what a/an _____ egg!"
                                          ADJECTIVE

From OFF-THE-WALL MAD LIBS® • Copyright © 2001, 1988, 1982, 1970 by Price Stern Sloan,
an imprint of Penguin Group (USA) Inc., 345 Hudson Street, New York, NY 10014.

MAD LIBS® is fun to play with friends, but you can also play it by yourself! To begin with, DO NOT look at the story on the page below. Fill in the blanks on this page with the words called for. Then, using the words you have selected, fill in the blank spaces in the story.

Now you've created your own hilarious MAD LIBS® game!

ALBERT EINSTEIN

CELEBRITY (MALE) _____

CELEBRITY (FEMALE) _____

NOUN _____

PLURAL NOUN _____

ADJECTIVE _____

PLURAL NOUN _____

ADJECTIVE _____

PLURAL NOUN _____

NOUN _____

A PLACE _____

PLURAL NOUN _____

NOUN _____

PROFESSION (PLURAL) _____

MAD LIBS
ALBERT EINSTEIN

Albert Einstein, the son of _____ and _____,
                              CELEBRITY (MALE)   CELEBRITY (FEMALE)

was born in Ulm, Germany, in 1879. In 1902, he had a job

as assistant _____ in the Swiss patent office and attended
                    NOUN

the University of Zurich. There he began studying atoms, molecules,

and _____. He developed his famous theory of
            PLURAL NOUN

_____ relativity, which expanded the phenomena of
    ADJECTIVE

subatomic _____ and _____ magnetism. In 1921,
              PLURAL NOUN   ADJECTIVE

he won the Nobel prize for _____ and was director of
                                  PLURAL NOUN

theoretical physics at the Kaiser Wilhelm _____ in Berlin.
                                                    NOUN

In 1933, when Hitler became Chancellor of _____,
                                                    A PLACE

Einstein came to America to take a post at Princeton Institute for

_____, where his theories helped America devise the first
    PLURAL NOUN

atomic _____. There is no question about it: Einstein was
            NOUN

one of the most brilliant _____ of our time.
                              PROFESSION (PLURAL)

From OFF-THE-WALL MAD LIBS® • Copyright © 2001, 1988, 1982, 1970 by Price Stern Sloan,
an imprint of Penguin Group (USA) Inc., 345 Hudson Street, New York, NY 10014.

MAD LIBS® is fun to play with friends, but you can also play it by yourself! To begin with, DO NOT look at the story on the page below. Fill in the blanks on this page with the words called for. Then, using the words you have selected, fill in the blank spaces in the story.

Now you've created your own hilarious MAD LIBS® game!

ROCK MUSIC

LAST NAME OF PERSON _____

ANOTHER LAST NAME _____

ADJECTIVE _____

PLURAL NOUN _____

PLURAL NOUN _____

ANIMAL (PLURAL) _____

CELEBRITY _____

PLURAL NOUN _____

PLURAL NOUN _____

NOUN _____

NOUN _____

PLURAL NOUN _____

MAD LIBS®
ROCK MUSIC

Young people today would rather listen to a good rock music concert

than to Johann Sebastian _____ or to Ludvig von
                          LAST NAME OF PERSON

_____ . Rock music is played by _____ groups
ANOTHER LAST NAME   ADJECTIVE

of young men who wear their hair below their _____ . They
                                              PLURAL NOUN

also wear very odd and colorful _____ and often have beards.
                                 PLURAL NOUN

The groups have attractive names such as "The _____"
                                               ANIMAL (PLURAL)

or " _____ and the Three _____ ." They usually
      CELEBRITY   PLURAL NOUN

play electric _____ . One member of the group usually sits
              PLURAL NOUN

on a raised platform and sets the rhythm by beating his _____ .
                                                         NOUN

The songs they sing are mostly about some fellow who has been

rejected by his _____ . They are very sad, and when young
                 NOUN

girls hear them, they often get tears in their _____ .
                                                PLURAL NOUN

From OFF-THE-WALL MAD LIBS® • Copyright © 2001, 1988, 1982, 1970 by Price Stern Sloan, an imprint of Penguin Group (USA) Inc., 345 Hudson Street, New York, NY 10014.

MAD LIBS® is fun to play with friends, but you can also play it by yourself! To begin with, DO NOT look at the story on the page below. Fill in the blanks on this page with the words called for. Then, using the words you have selected, fill in the blank spaces in the story.

Now you've created your own hilarious MAD LIBS® game!

BENJAMIN FRANKLIN

VERB _____

PLURAL NOUN _____

NOUN _____

NOUN _____

ADJECTIVE _____

ADVERB _____

ADJECTIVE _____

NOUN _____

NOUN _____

PLURAL NOUN _____

ADJECTIVE _____

SILLY WORD _____

MAD LIBS
BENJAMIN FRANKLIN

Benjamin Franklin left school at the age of 10 to _____ for
                                                        VERB

his father, who made candles, soap, and _____ in a little shop
                                              PLURAL NOUN

in Boston. In 1723, when Franklin was 17, he went to Philadelphia

carrying a loaf of _____ under his arm. He got a job as
                          NOUN

an apprentice _____ and soon became the editor of the
                     NOUN

Pennsylvania Gazette, a/an _____ publication. He worked
                                  ADJECTIVE

_____ and in 1732, he published the _____ book
     ADVERB   ADJECTIVE

called "Poor Richard's _____." He then became interested
                              NOUN

in science and, during a thunderstorm, he flew a/an _____
                                                          NOUN

attached to a string and proved that lightning and electricity were the

same thing. He also invented the harmonica and bifocal _____,
                                                              PLURAL NOUN

and started our postal service. In 1776, he became the American

Ambassador to France and did much to help the _____ cause
                                                      ADJECTIVE

of American liberty. Franklin was one of the most famous signers of

the Declaration of _____.
                        SILLY WORD

MAD LIBS® is fun to play with friends, but you can also play it by yourself! To begin with, DO NOT look at the story on the page below. Fill in the blanks on this page with the words called for. Then, using the words you have selected, fill in the blank spaces in the story.

Now you've created your own hilarious MAD LIBS® game!

NAPOLEON

NOUN _____

NOUN _____

ADJECTIVE _____

ADJECTIVE _____

ADJECTIVE _____

NOUN _____

ITALIAN WORD _____

PLURAL NOUN _____

ADJECTIVE _____

PLURAL NOUN _____

PLURAL NOUN _____

PLURAL NOUN _____

VERB (PAST TENSE) _____

OCCUPATION _____

ADJECTIVE _____

CITY _____

MAD LIBS
NAPOLEON

Although he was Emperor of France, Napoleon Bonaparte was actually

a Corsican, born on a small _____ in the Mediterranean
                              NOUN

Sea. When he was just 10 years old, Napoleon was sent to a military

_____ school in France, where his _____ stature
     NOUN   ADJECTIVE

earned him the nickname of "The _____ Corporal." At 24,
                                    ADJECTIVE

he was made a/an _____ general and married Josephine,
                     ADJECTIVE

the daughter of a well-known Parisian _____ . Soon after
                                            NOUN

that, he defeated the Italians at _____ and in 1804 was
                                      ITALIAN WORD

proclaimed emperor of all the _____ . But he made a/an
                                  PLURAL NOUN

_____ mistake and attacked Russia. He reached Moscow, but
   ADJECTIVE

the _____ had burned all their _____ and his men
      PLURAL NOUN   PLURAL NOUN

got frozen _____ . In 1814, he was _____ and
              PLURAL NOUN   VERB (PAST TENSE)

sent to Elba. But a year later, he came back to France and for 100 days

was again the _____ . However, he was defeated at Waterloo
                  OCCUPATION

and imprisoned on the island of St. Helena, a/an _____ place
                                                      ADJECTIVE

which resembled _____ .
                      CITY

MAD LIBS® is fun to play with friends, but you can also play it by yourself! To begin with, DO NOT look at the story on the page below. Fill in the blanks on this page with the words called for. Then, using the words you have selected, fill in the blank spaces in the story.

Now you've created your own hilarious MAD LIBS® game!

OUR SCHOOL

_____ SCHOOL

_____ ADJECTIVE (SUPERLATIVE)

_____ ADJECTIVE

_____ NUMBER

_____ NUMBER

_____ PLURAL NOUN

_____ SAME PLURAL NOUN

_____ ADJECTIVE

_____ PLURAL NOUN

_____ NOUN

_____ TYPE OF LIQUID

_____ CELEBRITY

_____ NOUN

_____ NOUN

_____ ADJECTIVE

MAD LIBS
OUR SCHOOL

_____ is one of America's _____
<u>SCHOOL</u>   <u>ADJECTIVE (SUPERLATIVE)</u>

institutions of _____ learning. The student body is composed
             <u>ADJECTIVE</u>

of _____ males and _____ _____ . The
   <u>NUMBER</u>   <u>NUMBER</u>   <u>PLURAL NOUN</u>

_____ get the best grades. Students can eat lunch in
<u>SAME PLURAL NOUN</u>

the _____ school cafeteria, which features boiled _____
    <u>ADJECTIVE</u>   <u>PLURAL NOUN</u>

and _____ sandwiches, with all the _____ they can
    <u>NOUN</u>   <u>TYPE OF LIQUID</u>

drink, for only 74 cents. The principal of the school, _____ ,
                                                        <u>CELEBRITY</u>

is raising money to build a new _____ laboratory and a new
                                <u>NOUN</u>

football _____ . Any student who goes to this school can
        <u>NOUN</u>

consider himself very _____ .
                      <u>ADJECTIVE</u>

MAD LIBS® is fun to play with friends, but you can also play it by yourself! To begin with, DO NOT look at the story on the page below. Fill in the blanks on this page with the words called for. Then, using the words you have selected, fill in the blank spaces in the story.

Now you've created your own hilarious MAD LIBS® game!

CHARLEMAGNE

ADJECTIVE _____

NATIONALITY (PLURAL) _____

NOUN _____

ADJECTIVE _____

NOUN _____

NOUN _____

PLURAL NOUN _____

PLURAL NOUN _____

TOWN _____

ADJECTIVE _____

PLURAL NOUN _____

ADJECTIVE _____

MAD LIBS
CHARLEMAGNE

Charlemagne was the _____ King of the Franks and

ADJECTIVE

_____ . In 800 A.D., he was crowned Emperor of the

NATIONALITY (PLURAL)

Holy Roman _____ by Pope Leo the Third. He was born in

NOUN

742. His father was Pepin the _____ , and his grandfather

ADJECTIVE

was Charles the _____ . Charlemagne converted thousands

NOUN

of Saxons, who were _____ worshippers, to Christianity. He

NOUN

converted them by cutting off their _____ and setting fire

PLURAL NOUN

to their _____ . In 778, he invaded Spain, but was defeated

PLURAL NOUN

by the Moors at _____ . Charlemagne was uneducated, but

TOWN

he had great respect for education and established many _____

ADJECTIVE

schools. And he was known for the justice of his _____ and

PLURAL NOUN

his kindness to _____ people.

ADJECTIVE

MAD LIBS® is fun to play with friends, but you can also play it by yourself! To begin with, DO NOT look at the story on the page below. Fill in the blanks on this page with the words called for. Then, using the words you have selected, fill in the blank spaces in the story.

Now you've created your own hilarious MAD LIBS® game!

GEORGE WASHINGTON CARVER

_____ ADJECTIVE

_____ NOUN

_____ PLURAL NOUN

_____ NOUN

_____ PLURAL NOUN

_____ TYPE OF FOOD

_____ PLACE

_____ ADJECTIVE

_____ PLURAL NOUN

George Washington Carver was a very _____ African American
                                      ADJECTIVE

scientist. He was in born a/an _____ in Missouri and graduated
                                NOUN

from Iowa State College with high _____ . He then worked at
                                    PLURAL NOUN

Tuskegee Institute as head of the _____ department and did
                                    NOUN

much research in the field of _____ . He discovered many
                                PLURAL NOUN

new uses for the peanut, the soybean, and the _____ .
                                              TYPE OF FOOD

He also improved the production of cotton and helped the entire

economy of _____ . George Washington Carver was looked
            PLACE

up to as an inspiration by all _____ people. His death in 1943
                                ADJECTIVE

was a loss to science and to _____ everywhere.
                              PLURAL NOUN

MAD LIBS® is fun to play with friends, but you can also play it by yourself! To begin with, DO NOT look at the story on the page below. Fill in the blanks on this page with the words called for. Then, using the words you have selected, fill in the blank spaces in the story.

Now you've created your own hilarious MAD LIBS® game!

HOW TO BE
A PHOTOGRAPHER

_____ ADJECTIVE

_____ PLURAL NOUN

_____ PLURAL NOUN

_____ ADJECTIVE

_____ NOUN

_____ NOUN

_____ ADJECTIVE

_____ NOUN

_____ PLURAL NOUN

_____ PLURAL NOUN

_____ ADVERB

_____ NUMBER

MAD LIBS
HOW TO BE
A PHOTOGRAPHER

Many _____ photographers make big money photographing
          ADJECTIVE

_____ and beautiful _____. They sell the prints
  PLURAL NOUN   PLURAL NOUN

to _____ magazines or to agencies who use them in
         ADJECTIVE

_____ advertisements. To be a photographer, you have to
      NOUN

have a/an _____ camera. You also need a/an _____
              NOUN   ADJECTIVE

meter and filters and a special close-up _____. Then you
                                              NOUN

either hire professional _____ or go out and snap candid
                           PLURAL NOUN

pictures of ordinary _____. But if you want to have a
                        PLURAL NOUN

career, you must study very _____ for at least _____ years.
                              ADVERB   NUMBER

MAD LIBS® is fun to play with friends, but you can also play it by yourself! To begin with, DO NOT look at the story on the page below. Fill in the blanks on this page with the words called for. Then, using the words you have selected, fill in the blank spaces in the story.

Now you've created your own hilarious MAD LIBS® game!

JULIUS CAESAR

LETTER OF THE ALPHABET _____

ADJECTIVE _____

PLURAL NOUN _____

ADVERB _____

GEOGRAPHICAL LOCATION _____

OCCUPATION _____

PART OF THE BODY _____

NOUN _____

ITALIAN WORD _____

NOUN _____

NOUN _____

FAMOUS PERSON (ITALIAN) _____

MAD LIBS®
JULIUS CAESAR

Julius Caesar was born in 102 B. _____ . He was a/an
LETTER OF THE ALPHABET

_____ general, and between 49 and 58 B.C. he defeated
ADJECTIVE

the Gauls, the Goths, and the _____ . After that, he
PLURAL NOUN

_____ became more famous and defeated Pompey at the battle
ADVERB

of _____ at Pharsala. The Romans then elected him
GEOGRAPHICAL LOCATION

permanent _____ , and he used to walk around wearing
OCCUPATION

a circlet of ivy leaves on his _____ . Then Caesar went to
PART OF THE BODY

Egypt, where he met Cleopatra, the teenage Egyptian _____ .
NOUN

When he conquered the Syrians in 46 B.C., he sent back a message

saying, "Veni, vedi, _____ ." In 44 B.C., a soothsayer told Caesar
ITALIAN WORD

to "Beware the Ides of _____ ," but he ignored the warning
NOUN

and in March he was stabbed in the _____ by a group of
NOUN

senators. His last words were, "Et tu, _____ ?"
FAMOUS PERSON (ITALIAN)

From OFF-THE-WALL MAD LIBS® • Copyright © 2001, 1988, 1982, 1970 by Price Stern Sloan,
an imprint of Penguin Group (USA) Inc., 345 Hudson Street, New York, NY 10014.

MAD LIBS® is fun to play with friends, but you can also play it by yourself! To begin with, DO NOT look at the story on the page below. Fill in the blanks on this page with the words called for. Then, using the words you have selected, fill in the blank spaces in the story.

Now you've created your own hilarious MAD LIBS® game!

LITTLE RED RIDING HOOD

COLOR _____

PLURAL NOUN _____

ADJECTIVE _____

EXCLAMATION _____

SILLY WORD _____

VERB (PAST TENSE) _____

PLURAL NOUN _____

VERB _____

PLURAL NOUN _____

VERB _____

PLURAL NOUN _____

MAD LIBS
LITTLE RED RIDING HOOD

One day, Little _____ Riding Hood was going through the
                        COLOR

forest carrying a basket of _____ for her grandmother.
                                  PLURAL NOUN

Suddenly, she met a big _____ wolf. "_____!"
                            ADJECTIVE   EXCLAMATION

said the wolf. "Where are you going, little _____?"
                                                  SILLY WORD

"I'm going to my grandmother's house," she said. Then the wolf

_____ away. When Miss Riding Hood got to her grand-
VERB (PAST TENSE)

mother's house, the wolf was in bed dressed like her grandmother.

"My, Grandmother," she said, "what big _____ you have."
                                            PLURAL NOUN

"The better to _____ you with," said the wolf. "And Grand-
                    VERB

mother," she said, "what big _____ you have." The wolf said,
                                  PLURAL NOUN

"The better to _____ you with." And then she said, "What
                    VERB

big _____ you have, Grandmother." But the wolf said
        PLURAL NOUN

nothing. He had just died of indigestion from eating Grandmother.

MAD LIBS® is fun to play with friends, but you can also play it by yourself! To begin with, DO NOT look at the story on the page below. Fill in the blanks on this page with the words called for. Then, using the words you have selected, fill in the blank spaces in the story.

Now you've created your own hilarious MAD LIBS® game!

INTRODUCTION TO A KIDDIE SHOW

_____ ADJECTIVE

_____ PERSON IN ROOM

_____ NUMBER

_____ PLURAL NOUN

_____ ANIMAL

_____ TYPE OF BIRD

_____ NONSENSE WORD

_____ NOUN

_____ LANGUAGE

_____ NOUN

_____ NUMBER

_____ ADJECTIVE

MAD LIBS

INTRODUCTION TO
A KIDDIE SHOW

Hi there, all you _____ little boys and girls! This is your
                     ADJECTIVE

old TV buddy, _____ , with another _____ -hour
                PERSON IN ROOM   NUMBER

program of fun and films and _____ for all of you. And we
                                 PLURAL NOUN

have a lot of great cartoons and videos. We will start with a cartoon

about Mickey _____ and Donald _____. Then
                  ANIMAL   TYPE OF BIRD

we'll have a commercial for a new toy called _____.
                                                NONSENSE WORD

It will teach you how to build a/an _____ and how to speak
                                        NOUN

_____ before you even start school. Next, we'll have a
    LANGUAGE

cartoon about Bullwinkle and Rocky, the flying _____. And
                                                    NOUN

after that, _____ more _____ commercials. Wow!
               NUMBER   ADJECTIVE

MAD LIBS® is fun to play with friends, but you can also play it by yourself! To begin with, DO NOT look at the story on the page below. Fill in the blanks on this page with the words called for. Then, using the words you have selected, fill in the blank spaces in the story.

Now you've created your own hilarious MAD LIBS® game!

THE THREE LITTLE PIGS

ADJECTIVE_____

PLURAL NOUN_____

ADVERB_____

PLURAL NOUN_____

ADJECTIVE_____

PLURAL NOUN_____

TYPE OF LIQUID_____

VERB (PAST TENSE)_____

VERB (PAST TENSE)_____

NOUN_____

VERB (PAST TENSE)_____

NOUN_____

PLURAL NOUN_____

MAD LIBS

THE THREE LITTLE PIGS

Once upon a time, there were three little pigs who decided to build

themselves houses. The first pig was _____, and he built
ADJECTIVE

his house out of _____. The second pig worked very
PLURAL NOUN

_____ and built a house out of _____. But
ADVERB PLURAL NOUN

the third pig was _____. He built his house out of
ADJECTIVE

_____ and _____. Then one day a big wolf came
PLURAL NOUN TYPE OF LIQUID

along. When he saw the first pig's house, he _____ and he
VERB (PAST TENSE)

_____ until he blew it down. Then he blew down the
VERB (PAST TENSE)

second pig's _____. But no matter how hard he _____,
NOUN VERB (PAST TENSE)

he couldn't blow down the third pig's _____.
NOUN

MORAL: Once the _____ come home to roost, it's too late
PLURAL NOUN

to whitewash the walls.

From OFF-THE-WALL MAD LIBS® • Copyright © 2001, 1988, 1982, 1970 by Price Stern Sloan,
an imprint of Penguin Group (USA) Inc., 345 Hudson Street, New York, NY 10014.

MAD LIBS® is fun to play with friends, but you can also play it by yourself! To begin with, DO NOT look at the story on the page below. Fill in the blanks on this page with the words called for. Then, using the words you have selected, fill in the blank spaces in the story.

Now you've created your own hilarious MAD LIBS® game!

THE POOR SPOTTED AUK

PLURAL NOUN _____

PLURAL NOUN _____

ADJECTIVE _____

ADJECTIVE _____

ANIMAL _____

PLURAL NOUN _____

PLURAL NOUN _____

NOUN _____

ADJECTIVE _____

ADJECTIVE _____

MAD LIBS
THE POOR SPOTTED AUK

The auk is a bird which will soon be extinct because hunters keep

shooting it so they can sell its _____ to women who wear
                                    PLURAL NOUN

them on their _____ . The government should establish
                 PLURAL NOUN

_____ game preserves where auks can build nests and lay
      ADJECTIVE

eggs and where they would be safe from their natural enemies, the

_____ otter and the underwater _____ . Others
      ADJECTIVE   ANIMAL

sneak up and eat the poor auk's _____ . Of course, a female
                                   PLURAL NOUN

auk can lay five thousand _____ a year, and if they all hatched,
                             PLURAL NOUN

in a short time we would all be up to our _____ in auks.
                                              NOUN

Remember, a/an _____ auk is a/an _____ auk.
                  ADJECTIVE   ADJECTIVE

LINK TRAINERS AND FLYING

ADJECTIVE _____

NOUN _____

PLURAL NOUN _____

NOUN _____

PLURAL NOUN _____

NOUN _____

ADJECTIVE _____

NOUN _____

NOUN _____

NOUN _____

NOUN _____

COLOR _____

NUMBER _____

NUMBER _____

Now you've created your own hilarious MAD LIBS® game!

MAD LIBS® is fun to play with friends, but you can also play it by yourself! To begin with, DO NOT look at the story on the page below. Fill in the blanks on this page with the words called for. Then, using the words you have selected, fill in the blank spaces in the story.

MAD LIBS®
LINK TRAINERS AND FLYING

A Link Trainer is a/an _____ airplane that never leaves the
                          ADJECTIVE

_____ . It's used to teach beginning _____ the
      NOUN   PLURAL NOUN

principles of flying. It has a/an _____ and a full set of
                                       NOUN

_____ , just like a regular airplane. It can imitate any
   PLURAL NOUN

sort of aerial maneuver such as a loop-the-_____ or a/an
                                                  NOUN

_____ dive, and it is very safe. Nothing can happen to you
  ADJECTIVE

unless, of course, you forget to fasten your safety _____ .
                                                          NOUN

Then you might fall out on your _____ .
                                     NOUN

After a student passes the tests on the Link Trainer, he then gets into

a real plane and learns to taxi down the _____ . And he
                                                NOUN

learns to tell which way the _____ is blowing before he
                                  NOUN

takes off into the "wild _____ yonder!" Then, in no time,
                              COLOR

he learns to take off and is flying _____ miles per hour at a
                                         NUMBER

height of _____ feet. When he does this, he is a real pilot.
               NUMBER

From OFF-THE-WALL MAD LIBS® • Copyright © 2001, 1988, 1982, 1970 by Price Stern Sloan,
an imprint of Penguin Group (USA) Inc., 345 Hudson Street, New York, NY 10014.

MAD LIBS® is fun to play with friends, but you can also play it by yourself! To begin with, DO NOT look at the story on the page below. Fill in the blanks on this page with the words called for. Then, using the words you have selected, fill in the blank spaces in the story.

Now you've created your own hilarious MAD LIBS® game!

FIREFIGHTERS

ADJECTIVE _____

ADJECTIVE _____

NOUN _____

NOUN _____

PLURAL NOUN _____

NUMBER _____

PLURAL NOUN _____

NOUN _____

NOUN _____

ADJECTIVE _____

TYPE OF LIQUID _____

PLURAL NOUN _____

ADJECTIVE _____

NOUN _____

PLURAL NOUN _____

NOUN _____

MAD LIBS

FIREFIGHTERS

When I was ten years old, my _____ ambition in life was
                                   ADJECTIVE

to be a firefighter—but here I am, nothing but a/an _____
                                                         ADJECTIVE

_____ . If I were a firefighter, I'd get to wear a huge, red
      NOUN

_____ . And I could ride on the fire engines that carry 80-foot
    NOUN

_____ and travel _____ miles an hour. When fire engines
    PLURAL NOUN   NUMBER

blow their _____ , all cars have to pull over to the side of
              PLURAL NOUN

the _____ . Fire departments have hook and _____
      NOUN   NOUN

wagons as well as pump trucks which carry _____ hoses
                                               ADJECTIVE

that pump _____ into burning _____ .
             TYPE OF LIQUID   PLURAL NOUN

firefighters have to go into _____ buildings and fight their way
                                 ADJECTIVE

through smoke and _____ to rescue any _____
                        NOUN   PLURAL NOUN

who may be trapped inside. We should all be thankful that our

firefighters are on the job twenty-four hours a/an _____ .
                                                         NOUN

From OFF-THE-WALL MAD LIBS® • Copyright © 2001, 1988, 1982, 1970 by Price Stern Sloan,
an imprint of Penguin Group (USA) Inc., 345 Hudson Street, New York, NY 10014.

MAD LIBS® is fun to play with friends, but you can also play it by yourself! To begin with, DO NOT look at the story on the page below. Fill in the blanks on this page with the words called for. Then, using the words you have selected, fill in the blank spaces in the story.

Now you've created your own hilarious MAD LIBS® game!

SMOKING CIGARETTES

TYPE OF DISEASE _____

NOUN _____

PART OF THE BODY _____

ADJECTIVE _____

PERSON IN ROOM _____

PLURAL NOUN _____

PLURAL NOUN _____

NASTY ADJECTIVE _____

PLURAL NOUN _____

EXCLAMATION _____

PLURAL NOUN _____

MAD LIBS®
SMOKING CIGARETTES

Medical science has discovered that smoking cigarettes causes

_____. It is also bad for your _____ and causes
TYPE OF DISEASE   NOUN

pains in the _____. When mice and dogs were exposed
              PART OF THE BODY

to _____ cigarette smoke, they developed _____'s
    ADJECTIVE   PERSON IN ROOM

disease. Tobacco companies have put charcoal _____ on
                                              PLURAL NOUN

the ends of cigarettes, but they still spend millions of _____
                                                          PLURAL NOUN

advertising their _____ product. If you smoke cigarettes,
                   NASTY ADJECTIVE

the tobacco will leave all kinds of tar and _____ in your
                                             PLURAL NOUN

lungs. This will make you cough and say, "_____!"
                                           EXCLAMATION

Don't smoke cigarettes. Remember, only _____ smoke.
                                        PLURAL NOUN

From OFF-THE-WALL MAD LIBS® • Copyright © 2001, 1988, 1982, 1970 by Price Stern Sloan,
an imprint of Penguin Group (USA) Inc., 345 Hudson Street, New York, NY 10014.

GOOFY MAD LIBS

by Roger Price & Leonard Stern

PSS!

PRICE STERN SLOAN

An Imprint of Penguin Group (USA) Inc.

PRICE STERN SLOAN
Penguin Group (USA) Inc., 375 Hudson Street, New York, New York 10014, USA
Penguin Group (Canada), 90 Eglinton Avenue East, Suite 700,
Toronto, Ontario M4P 2Y3, Canada (a division of Pearson Penguin Canada Inc.)
Penguin Books Ltd, 80 Strand, London WC2R 0RL, England
Penguin Ireland, 25 St Stephen's Green, Dublin 2, Ireland
(a division of Penguin Books Ltd)
Penguin Group (Australia), 707 Collins Street, Melbourne, Victoria 3008, Australia
(a division of Pearson Australia Group Pty Ltd)
Penguin Books India Pvt Ltd, 11 Community Centre,
Panchsheel Park, New Delhi—110 017, India
Penguin Group (NZ), 67 Apollo Drive, Rosedale, Auckland 0632, New Zealand
(a division of Pearson New Zealand Ltd)
Penguin Books, Rosebank Office Park, 181 Jan Smuts Avenue,
Parktown North 2193, South Africa
Penguin China, B7 Jaiming Center, 27 East Third Ring Road North,
Chaoyang District, Beijing 100020, China

Penguin Books Ltd, Registered Offices:
80 Strand, London WC2R 0RL, England

Published by Price Stern Sloan, a division of Penguin Young Readers Group,
345 Hudson Street, New York, New York 10014.

ISBN 0-8431-0059-1

MAD☺LIBS®
INSTRUCTIONS

MAD LIBS® is a game for people who don't like games!
It can be played by one, two, three, four, or forty.

●RIDICULOUSLY SIMPLE DIRECTIONS

In this tablet you will find stories containing blank spaces where words are left out. One player, the READER, selects one of these stories. The READER does not tell anyone what the story is about. Instead, he/she asks the other players, the WRITERS, to give him/her words. These words are used to fill in the blank spaces in the story.

●TO PLAY

The READER asks each WRITER in turn to call out a word—an adjective or a noun or whatever the space calls for—and uses them to fill in the blank spaces in the story. The result is a MAD LIBS® game.

When the READER then reads the completed MAD LIBS® game to the other players, they will discover that they have written a story that is fantastic, screamingly funny, shocking, silly, crazy, or just plain dumb—depending upon which words each WRITER called out.

●EXAMPLE (*Before* and *After*)

"_____!" he said _____
　　　　　EXCLAMATION　　　　　　　　　　　　　　　ADVERB

as he jumped into his convertible _____ and
　　　　　　　　　　　　　　　　　　　　NOUN

drove off with his _____ wife.
　　　　　　　　　ADJECTIVE

"_____*Ouch*_____!" he said _____*stupidly*_____
　　　EXCLAMATION　　　　　　　　　　　ADVERB

as he jumped into his convertible _____*cat*_____ and
　　　　　　　　　　　　　　　　NOUN

drove off with his _____*brave*_____ wife.
　　　　　　　　ADJECTIVE

In case you have forgotten what adjectives, adverbs, nouns, and verbs are, here is a quick review:

An ADJECTIVE describes something or somebody. *Lumpy*, *soft*, *ugly*, *messy*, and *short* are adjectives.

An ADVERB tells how something is done. It modifies a verb and usually ends in "ly." *Modestly*, *stupidly*, *greedily*, and *carefully* are adverbs.

A NOUN is the name of a person, place, or thing. *Sidewalk*, *umbrella*, *bridle*, *bathtub*, and *nose* are nouns.

A VERB is an action word. *Run*, *pitch*, *jump*, and *swim* are verbs. Put the verbs in past tense if the directions say PAST TENSE. *Ran*, *pitched*, *jumped*, and *swam* are verbs in the past tense.

When we ask for A PLACE, we mean any sort of place: a country or city (*Spain*, *Cleveland*) or a room (*bathroom*, *kitchen*).

An EXCLAMATION or SILLY WORD is any sort of funny sound, gasp, grunt, or outcry, like *Wow!*, *Ouch!*, *Whomp!*, *Ick!*, and *Gadzooks!*

When we ask for specific words, like a NUMBER, a COLOR, an ANIMAL, or a PART OF THE BODY, we mean a word that is one of those things, like *seven*, *blue*, *horse*, or *head*.

When we ask for a PLURAL, it means more than one. For example, *cat* pluralized is *cats*.

MAD LIBS® is fun to play with friends, but you can also play it by yourself! To begin with, DO NOT look at the story on the page below. Fill in the blanks on this page with the words called for. Then, using the words you have selected, fill in the blank spaces in the story.

Now you've created your own hilarious MAD LIBS® game!

AMUSEMENT PARKS

NOUN _____

ARTICLE OF CLOTHING _____

ADJECTIVE _____

ADJECTIVE _____

NOUN _____

PLURAL NOUN _____

NOUN _____

ADJECTIVE _____

TYPE OF FOOD _____

TYPE OF LIQUID _____

PART OF THE BODY _____

PLURAL NOUN _____

PLURAL NOUN _____

ANIMAL _____

NOUN _____

MAD LIBS®
AMUSEMENT PARKS

An amusement park is always fun to visit on a hot summer _____ .
NOUN

When you get there, you can wear your _____ and go
ARTICLE OF CLOTHING

for a swim. And there are lots of _____ things to eat. You can
ADJECTIVE

start off with a/an _____ -dog on a/an _____ with
ADJECTIVE   NOUN

mustard, relish, and _____ on it. Then you can have a
PLURAL NOUN

buttered ear of _____ with a nice _____ slice of
NOUN   ADJECTIVE

_____ and a big bottle of cold _____ . When you
TYPE OF FOOD   TYPE OF LIQUID

are full, it's time to go on the roller coaster, which should settle your

_____ . Other amusement park rides are the bumper cars,
PART OF THE BODY

which have little _____ that you drive and run into other
PLURAL NOUN

_____ , and the merry-go-round, where you can sit on a big
PLURAL NOUN

_____ and try to grab the gold _____ as you ride past it.
ANIMAL   NOUN

From GOOFY MAD LIBS® • Copyright © 2001, 1988 by Price Stern Sloan,
an imprint of Penguin Group (USA) Inc., 345 Hudson Street, New York, NY 10014.

MAD LIBS® is fun to play with friends, but you can also play it by yourself! To begin with, DO NOT look at the story on the page below. Fill in the blanks on this page with the words called for. Then, using the words you have selected, fill in the blank spaces in the story.

Now you've created your own hilarious MAD LIBS® game!

BULL FIGHTING

ADJECTIVE _____

GEOGRAPHICAL LOCATION _____

NOUN _____

SPANISH WORD _____

ARTICLE OF CLOTHING _____

SAME ARTICLE OF CLOTHING _____

ADJECTIVE _____

ADJECTIVE _____

PART OF THE BODY _____

ANOTHER SPANISH WORD _____

PLURAL NOUN _____

EXCLAMATION _____

ADJECTIVE _____

PLURAL NOUN _____

MAD LIBS®
BULL FIGHTING

Bullfighting is a/an _____ sport which is very popular in
                          ADJECTIVE

_____ . A bullfighter is called a *matador*, and his
     GEOGRAPHICAL LOCATION

equipment consists of a long, sharp _____ called a/an
                                              NOUN

"_____" and a bright red _____ . He
     SPANISH WORD   ARTICLE OF CLOTHING

waves his _____ at the bull, which makes the bull
     SAME ARTICLE OF CLOTHING

_____ and causes him to charge. The matador then goes
     ADJECTIVE

through a series of _____ maneuvers to avoid getting
                          ADJECTIVE

caught on the bull's _____ . If the matador kills the
                        PART OF THE BODY

bull, the spectators yell, "_____!" and throw
                             ANOTHER SPANISH WORD

their _____ into the ring. If the bull wins, they yell
          PLURAL NOUN

"_____!" and call for another matador. Bullfighting
     EXCLAMATION

is a very _____ sport, but it will never be popular in America
          ADJECTIVE

because Americans don't believe in cruelty to _____ .
                                                  PLURAL NOUN

MAD LIBS® is fun to play with friends, but you can also play it by yourself! To begin with, DO NOT look at the story on the page below. Fill in the blanks on this page with the words called for. Then, using the words you have selected, fill in the blank spaces in the story.

Now you've created your own hilarious MAD LIBS® game!

BOWLING

PLACE _____

ADJECTIVE _____

PLURAL NOUN _____

ADJECTIVE _____

NOUN _____

NUMBER _____

FUNNY NOISE _____

ANOTHER FUNNY NOISE _____

NOUN _____

PLURAL NOUN _____

NOUN _____

PART OF THE BODY _____

MAD LIBS®
BOWLING

Almost every community in America now has a bowling _____
PLACE

because bowling has become very _____ with young
ADJECTIVE

_____. Most of them become very _____
PLURAL NOUN   ADJECTIVE

at the game. The main object of the game is to roll a heavy bowling

_____ down the alley and knock down the _____ pins
NOUN   NUMBER

which are at the other end. If you knock them down in one roll, it's

called a/an "_____." If it take two rolls, it's called a/an
FUNNY NOISE

"_____." Many alleys have automatic _____
ANOTHER FUNNY NOISE   NOUN

setters. Others hire _____ who set the pins by _____.
PLURAL NOUN   NOUN

The most important thing to remember when bowling is to make

sure you have a good grip on the _____ or you're liable to
NOUN

drop it on your _____!
PART OF THE BODY

From GOOFY MAD LIBS® • Copyright © 2001, 1988 by Price Stern Sloan,
an imprint of Penguin Group (USA) Inc., 345 Hudson Street, New York, NY 10014.

MAD LIBS® is fun to play with friends, but you can also play it by yourself! To begin with, **DO NOT** look at the story on the page below. Fill in the blanks on this page with the words called for. Then, using the words you have selected, fill in the blank spaces in the story.

Now you've created your own hilarious MAD LIBS® game!

A VISIT TO THE ZOO

PLURAL NOUN _____

PLURAL NOUN _____

ADJECTIVE _____

TYPE OF LIQUID _____

ANIMAL (PLURAL) _____

ADJECTIVE _____

FUNNY NOISE _____

ANOTHER FUNNY NOISE _____

ADJECTIVE _____

PLURAL NOUN _____

ANIMAL _____

ANOTHER ANIMAL _____

PART OF THE BODY _____

PLURAL NOUN _____

ADJECTIVE _____

MAD LIBS®
A VISIT TO THE ZOO

Zoos are places where wild _____ are kept in pens or cages
PLURAL NOUN

so that _____ can come and look at them. There are two
PLURAL NOUN

zoos in New York, one in the Bronx and one in _____ Park.
ADJECTIVE

The park zoo is built around a large pond filled with clear sparkling

_____. You will see several _____ swimming in the
TYPE OF LIQUID   ANIMAL (PLURAL)

pond and eating fish. When it is feeding time, all of the animals make

_____ noises. The elephant goes "_____" and the
ADJECTIVE   FUNNY NOISE

turtledoves go "_____." In one part of the zoo, there
ANOTHER FUNNY NOISE

are _____ gorillas who love to eat _____. In another
ADJECTIVE   PLURAL NOUN

building, there is a spotted African _____ that is so fast it
ANIMAL

can outrun a/an _____. But my favorite animal is the
ANOTHER ANIMAL

hippopotamus. It has a huge _____ and eats fifty pounds
PART OF THE BODY

of _____ a day. You would never know that, technically, it's
PLURAL NOUN

nothing but an oversized _____ pig.
ADJECTIVE

MAD LIBS® is fun to play with friends, but you can also play it by yourself! To begin with, DO NOT look at the story on the page below. Fill in the blanks on this page with the words called for. Then, using the words you have selected, fill in the blank spaces in the story.

Now you've created your own hilarious MAD LIBS® game!

LITTLE LEAGUE BASEBALL

PLURAL NOUN _____

PLURAL NOUN _____

NUMBER _____

NUMBER _____

NOUN _____

ADJECTIVE _____

PLURAL NOUN _____

ADJECTIVE _____

ADJECTIVE _____

PART OF THE BODY _____

NOUN _____

OCCUPATION (PLURAL) _____

PERSON IN ROOM _____

MAD LIBS®
LITTLE LEAGUE BASEBALL

Many future Big League baseball _____ are being trained
<u>PLURAL NOUN</u>

in Little League today. The Little Leagues are just like the Big League

_____ , except that the players are all between _____
<u>PLURAL NOUN</u>   <u>NUMBER</u>

and _____ years old. When a/an _____ goes out for a
<u>NUMBER</u>   <u>NOUN</u>

Little League team, he is given _____ tests in fielding fast
<u>ADJECTIVE</u>

_____ and in hitting. He can either play in the _____-
<u>PLURAL NOUN</u>   <u>ADJECTIVE</u>

field or in the _____-field. Or if he has a good throwing
<u>ADJECTIVE</u>

_____ , he can be a pitcher or catcher. If he can't do
<u>PART OF THE BODY</u>

anything, he can sit on the _____ . But no matter what
<u>NOUN</u>

position he plays, a Little Leaguer learns to work with his fellow

_____ . If you play with a Little League team, who
<u>OCCUPATION (PLURAL)</u>

knows, you may become a famous Big League baseball player like

_____ .
<u>PERSON IN ROOM</u>

MAD LIBS® is fun to play with friends, but you can also play it by yourself! To begin with, DO NOT look at the story on the page below. Fill in the blanks on this page with the words called for. Then, using the words you have selected, fill in the blank spaces in the story.

Now you've created your own hilarious MAD LIBS® game!

CONCERT PROGRAM

PERSON IN ROOM _____

PLURAL NOUN _____

ADJECTIVE _____

NOUN _____

ADJECTIVE _____

PLURAL NOUN _____

ADJECTIVE _____

NOUN _____

ADJECTIVE _____

NOUN _____

MUSICAL INSTRUMENT _____

NUMBER _____

ADJECTIVE _____

NOUN _____

NOUN _____

MAD LIBS®
CONCERT PROGRAM

This evening, the famous orchestra conductor, _____ ,
                                                PERSON IN ROOM

will present a program of classical _____ at the _____
                                     PLURAL NOUN   ADJECTIVE

music center. He/She will conduct the _____ Symphony
                                            NOUN

Orchestra, which is noted for its excellent string and _____
                                                            ADJECTIVE

wind sections, considered by many _____ to be the
                                      PLURAL NOUN

world's most _____ ensemble. The program will begin with
              ADJECTIVE

Debussy's "Clair de _____," followed by Mendelssohn's
                         NOUN

"_____ Song," and Strauss' "Tales of the Vienna _____."
   ADJECTIVE   NOUN

Then we will hear Rachmaninoff's "_____ Concerto
                                   MUSICAL INSTRUMENT

Number _____," but only the _____ movements.
        NUMBER   ADJECTIVE

After intermission, the second half of the program will be devoted to

a playing in its entirety of Beethoven's "Fifth _____." Tickets
                                                    NOUN

are on sale now at the _____ office.
                           NOUN

MAD LIBS® is fun to play with friends, but you can also play it by yourself! To begin with, DO NOT look at the story on the page below. Fill in the blanks on this page with the words called for. Then, using the words you have selected, fill in the blank spaces in the story.

Now you've created your own hilarious MAD LIBS® game!

CONTEST

_____ ADJECTIVE

_____ ADJECTIVE

_____ ADJECTIVE

_____ NUMBER

_____ PERSON IN ROOM

_____ NOUN

_____ ADVERB

_____ NOUN

_____ TYPE OF FOOD

_____ NOUN

_____ NOUN

_____ PLURAL NOUN

_____ NOUN

_____ PLURAL NOUN

_____ YEAR

_____ PLURAL NOUN

MAD LIBS
CONTEST

Now is your chance to enter this _____ contest. Anyone,
                                        ADJECTIVE

and we mean anyone, can enter this _____ contest. Just
                                          ADJECTIVE

follow these _____ rules:
                  ADJECTIVE

Write down in _____ words or less why you think that
                   NUMBER

_____ should be elected "_____ of the Year."
   PERSON IN ROOM   NOUN

Remember, he/she does not know that you think so _____
                                                        ADVERB

of him/her. First prize will be a deluxe three-speed _____ ,
                                                          NOUN

plus a year's supply of _____ . Second prize is a 21-foot
                           TYPE OF FOOD

_____ . Third prize is a full-color _____ , plus a set
    NOUN   NOUN

of _____ . Each entry must be accompanied by a stamped,
     PLURAL NOUN

self-addressed _____ . Decision of the _____
                     NOUN   PLURAL NOUN

will be announced in _____ and will be final. In the event of a
                          YEAR

tie, duplicate _____ will be awarded.
                   PLURAL NOUN

MAD LIBS® is fun to play with friends, but you can also play it by yourself! To begin with, **DO NOT** look at the story on the page below. Fill in the blanks on this page with the words called for. Then, using the words you have selected, fill in the blank spaces in the story.

Now you've created your own hilarious MAD LIBS® game!

MY MUSIC LESSON

_____
NOUN

_____
CELEBRITY (FEMALE)

_____
NOUN

_____
PLURAL NOUN

_____
ADJECTIVE

_____
NOUN

_____
PERIOD OF TIME

_____
PLURAL NOUN

_____
CELEBRITY (LAST NAME)

_____
NOUN

_____
PART OF THE BODY

_____
PROFESSION

_____
TYPE OF BUILDING

MAD LIBS®
MY MUSIC LESSON

Every Wednesday, when I get home from school, I have a piano

lesson. My teacher is a very strict _____ . Her name is
                                            NOUN

_____ . Our piano is a Steinway Concert _____
CELEBRITY (FEMALE)   NOUN

and it has 88 _____ . It also has a soft pedal and a/an
                    PLURAL NOUN

_____ pedal. When I have a lesson, I sit down on the piano
  ADJECTIVE

_____ and play for _____ . I do scales to
     NOUN   PERIOD OF TIME

exercise my _____ , and then I usually play a minuet by
                 PLURAL NOUN

Johann Sebastian _____ . Teacher says I am a natural
                       CELEBRITY (LAST NAME)

_____ and have a good musical _____ . Perhaps
  NOUN   PART OF THE BODY

when I get better I will become a concert _____ and give
                                                PROFESSION

a recital at Carnegie _____ .
                          TYPE OF BUILDING

MAD LIBS® is fun to play with friends, but you can also play it by yourself! To begin with, DO NOT look at the story on the page below. Fill in the blanks on this page with the words called for. Then, using the words you have selected, fill in the blank spaces in the story.

Now you've created your own hilarious MAD LIBS® game!

THE FARMER

PLURAL NOUN _____

NOUN _____

PLURAL NOUN _____

ADJECTIVE _____

PLURAL NOUN _____

ADJECTIVE _____

TYPE OF LIQUID _____

PLURAL NOUN _____

NOUN _____

PLURAL NOUN _____

ADJECTIVE _____

Farmers work very hard planting wheat and _____ . They

PLURAL NOUN

begin by plowing their _____ , and if they don't have a

NOUN

tractor, they use _____ . Then they plant _____

PLURAL NOUN · ADJECTIVE

seeds, and by the next fall, they have many acres of _____ .

PLURAL NOUN

Tomatoes are harder to raise. They grow on _____ bushes

ADJECTIVE

and the farmer sprays them with _____ to keep the bugs

TYPE OF LIQUID

off. The easiest things to grow are green _____ , but the

PLURAL NOUN

farmer must be very careful to make sure worms don't get into his

_____ . Farmers also raise onions, cabbages, lettuce, and

NOUN

_____ . But no matter what they grow, farmers really lead

PLURAL NOUN

a/an _____ life.

ADJECTIVE

MAD LIBS® is fun to play with friends, but you can also play it by yourself! To begin with, DO NOT look at the story on the page below. Fill in the blanks on this page with the words called for. Then, using the words you have selected, fill in the blank spaces in the story.

Now you've created your own hilarious MAD LIBS® game!

HISTORY OF
A FAMOUS INVENTION

NOUN _____

ADJECTIVE _____

FAMOUS PERSON _____

ANOTHER FAMOUS PERSON _____

NOUN _____

PLURAL NOUN _____

EXCLAMATION _____

NOUN _____

ADJECTIVE _____

PLURAL NOUN _____

NOUN _____

TYPE OF FOOD (PLURAL) _____

TYPE OF LIQUID _____

NOUN _____

ADJECTIVE _____

NUMBER _____

ADVERB _____

MAD LIBS
HISTORY OF
A FAMOUS INVENTION

The first electric _____ was invented in 1904 by a/an
                              NOUN

_____ young man named _____. He and his
  ADJECTIVE   FAMOUS PERSON

brother _____ ran a small _____-repair shop,
         ANOTHER FAMOUS PERSON   NOUN

and in their spare time they studied _____. When they
                                          PLURAL NOUN

started work on their invention, everyone said, " _____!
                                                      EXCLAMATION

You'll never get it off the _____." But they built a/an
                                    NOUN

_____ model out of old _____ and a used _____.
 ADJECTIVE   PLURAL NOUN   NOUN

The model worked fine, and in ten minutes it toasted 24 slices of

_____. It also used up two gallons of _____
 TYPE OF FOOD (PLURAL)   TYPE OF LIQUID

an hour, and the top converted into a/an _____. They sold the
                                              NOUN

patent to a/an _____ millionaire for _____ dollars and
                 ADJECTIVE   NUMBER

lived _____ ever after.
        ADVERB

From GOOFY MAD LIBS® • Copyright © 2001, 1988 by Price Stern Sloan,
an imprint of Penguin Group (USA) Inc., 345 Hudson Street, New York, NY 10014.

MAD LIBS® is fun to play with friends, but you can also play it by yourself! To begin with, DO NOT look at the story on the page below. Fill in the blanks on this page with the words called for. Then, using the words you have selected, fill in the blank spaces in the story.

Now you've created your own hilarious MAD LIBS® game!

GEORGE WASHINGTON

NOUN_____

ADJECTIVE_____

ADJECTIVE_____

NOUN_____

NOUN_____

EXCLAMATION_____

VERB (PAST TENSE)_____

NOUN_____

NOUN_____

NOUN_____

NOUN_____

NOUN_____

OCCUPATION_____

MAD LIBS

GEORGE WASHINGTON

George Washington, the father of our _____ , was a very
NOUN

_____ man. When George was a/an _____ boy,
ADJECTIVE   ADJECTIVE

he took his _____ and chopped down his father's favorite
NOUN

cherry _____ . "_____ !" said his father. "Who
NOUN   EXCLAMATION

has _____ my _____ ?" Then he saw George
VERB (PAST TENSE)   NOUN

holding a sharp _____ in his hand. "Father," said George,
NOUN

"I cannot tell a lie. I did it with my little _____ ." His father
NOUN

smiled and patted little George on the _____ . "You are a very
NOUN

honest _____ ," he said, "and some day you may become the
NOUN

first _____ of the United States."
OCCUPATION

MAD LIBS® is fun to play with friends, but you can also play it by yourself! To begin with, DO NOT look at the story on the page below. Fill in the blanks on this page with the words called for. Then, using the words you have selected, fill in the blank spaces in the story.

Now you've created your own hilarious MAD LIBS® game!

THE AMAZING RANDY

PLURAL NOUN _____

NOUN _____

NOUN _____

NOUN _____

ANIMAL _____

NOUN _____

NOUN _____

ADJECTIVE _____

NOUN _____

ADJECTIVE _____

TYPE OF LIQUID _____

ANOTHER TYPE OF LIQUID _____

ADJECTIVE _____

NOUN _____

FUNNY WORD _____

MAD LIBS
THE AMAZING RANDY

Recently on TV, I saw an amazing magician and escape artist. Both of

his _____ were laced up in a straitjacket, and he was
　　　　PLURAL NOUN

suspended by a/an _____ 60 feet in the air over a busy
　　　　　　　　　　　NOUN

_____. And he escaped! A man who can do that must be a real
NOUN

_____. I saw a magician once who put a/an _____
　　NOUN　　　　　　　　　　　　　　　　　　　　　　　ANIMAL

in a/an _____ and then waved his magic _____ and
　　　　　NOUN　　　　　　　　　　　　　　　　　　NOUN

made it disappear. I saw another _____ magician who sawed
　　　　　　　　　　　　　　　　　ADJECTIVE

a beautiful _____ in half right on the stage. If you practice hard,
　　　　　　NOUN

there are several _____ magic tricks you can learn to do. For
　　　　　　　　ADJECTIVE

instance, you can learn how to take a glass of _____ and
　　　　　　　　　　　　　　　　　　　　　TYPE OF LIQUID

turn it into _____. Or you can wave a/an _____
　　　ANOTHER TYPE OF LIQUID　　　　　　　　　　　　ADJECTIVE

wand in the air and make it turn into a red _____. All you have
　　　　　　　　　　　　　　　　　　　NOUN

to do is memorize the secret magic word, "_____."
　　　　　　　　　　　　　　　　　　　　FUNNY WORD

MAD LIBS® is fun to play with friends, but you can also play it by yourself! To begin with, DO NOT look at the story on the page below. Fill in the blanks on this page with the words called for. Then, using the words you have selected, fill in the blank spaces in the story.

Now you've created your own hilarious MAD LIBS® game!

A CHARMING STORY WITH A HAPPY ENDING

NOUN _____

ADJECTIVE _____

PLURAL NOUN _____

ADJECTIVE _____

PLURAL NOUN _____

ADJECTIVE _____

PLURAL NOUN _____

EXCLAMATION _____

VERB _____

VERB _____

NOUN _____

PLURAL NOUN _____

NOUN _____

VERB (PAST TENSE) _____

ADJECTIVE _____

MAD LIBS
A CHARMING STORY WITH A HAPPY ENDING

Once upon a/an _____, there were three little pigs. The
_____NOUN_____

first little pig was very _____, and he built a house for
_____ADJECTIVE

himself out of _____. The second little pig was
_____PLURAL NOUN

_____, and he built a house out of _____. But
____ADJECTIVE_____PLURAL NOUN

the third little pig was very _____, and he built his house
_____ADJECTIVE

out of genuine _____. Well one day, a mean old wolf
_____PLURAL NOUN

came along and saw the houses. "_____!" he said. "I'll
_____EXCLAMATION

_____ and I'll _____ and I'll blow your house
_____VERB_____VERB

down." And he blew down the first little pig's _____ and
_____NOUN

the second little pig's _____. The two little pigs ran
_____PLURAL NOUN

to the third pig's house. Thereupon, the wolf began blowing, but he

couldn't blow down the third little pig's _____ house. So he
_____NOUN

_____ off into the forest, and the three little _____
VERB (PAST TENSE)_____ADJECTIVE

pigs moved to Chicago and went into the sausage business.

From GOOFY MAD LIBS® • Copyright © 2001, 1988 by Price Stern Sloan,
an imprint of Penguin Group (USA) Inc., 345 Hudson Street, New York, NY 10014.

MAD LIBS® is fun to play with friends, but you can also play it by yourself! To begin with, DO NOT look at the story on the page below. Fill in the blanks on this page with the words called for. Then, using the words you have selected, fill in the blank spaces in the story.

Now you've created your own hilarious MAD LIBS® game!

WEATHER REPORT

PLURAL NOUN _____

NUMBER _____

ADJECTIVE _____

ADJECTIVE _____

ADVERB _____

ADJECTIVE _____

GEOGRAPHICAL LOCATION _____

ADJECTIVE _____

ANOTHER GEOGRAPHICAL LOCATION _____

ADJECTIVE _____

ADJECTIVE _____

ADJECTIVE _____

PLURAL NOUN _____

ARTICLE OF CLOTHING _____

ANOTHER ARTICLE OF CLOTHING _____

MAD LIBS®
WEATHER REPORT

Good evening, ladies and _____. Let's take a look at the

PLURAL NOUN

weather picture. Right now the temperature is _____ degrees

NUMBER

and there are _____ winds coming from the west. However,

ADJECTIVE

according to a report just received, a/an _____ front is moving

ADJECTIVE

down from Canada. This _____ moving mass of _____

ADVERB · ADJECTIVE

air is headed directly for _____ and should result in

GEOGRAPHICAL LOCATION

a/an _____ pressure area over _____

ADJECTIVE · ANOTHER GEOGRAPHICAL LOCATION

by early morning. Tomorrow we can expect temperatures in the

_____ forties. Also, it will generally be _____ and

ADJECTIVE · ADJECTIVE

_____ with a chance of scattered _____ near the coast.

ADJECTIVE · PLURAL NOUN

If you are going out, be sure and wear your _____

ARTICLE OF CLOTHING

and a heavier _____, just in case.

ANOTHER ARTICLE OF CLOTHING

From GOOFY MAD LIBS® • Copyright © 2001, 1988 by Price Stern Sloan,
an imprint of Penguin Group (USA) Inc., 345 Hudson Street, New York, NY 10014.

MAD LIBS® is fun to play with friends, but you can also play it by yourself! To begin with, DO NOT look at the story on the page below. Fill in the blanks on this page with the words called for. Then, using the words you have selected, fill in the blank spaces in the story.

Now you've created your own hilarious MAD LIBS® game!

INDIA

_____
ADJECTIVE

_____
PLURAL NOUN

_____
PLACE

_____
ADJECTIVE

_____
PLURAL NOUN

_____
PLURAL NOUN

_____
PLURAL NOUN

_____
NOUN

_____
ADVERB

_____
ADJECTIVE

_____
NOUN

_____
PLURAL NOUN

MAD LIBS®
INDIA

India is a very _____ country located almost directly across
                         ADJECTIVE

the world from the United _____ of America. India is
                                  PLURAL NOUN

bounded on the north by _____ and on the south by the
                                 PLACE

_____ Ocean. Indian women are very beautiful and wear a
      ADJECTIVE

lot of large _____ on their arms and often wear large strings
                 PLURAL NOUN

of _____ around their necks. They have many religious sects,
     PLURAL NOUN

including Hindus, Brahmin, Muslims, and _____. Many
                                                PLURAL NOUN

Indians regard the cow as a sacred _____ , and cows are
                                              NOUN

allowed to wander _____ about the streets. One Indian caste
                         ADVERB

is called the Untouchables. The _____ Untouchables sit in
                                        ADJECTIVE

the city _____ and beg tourists to give them _____ .
              NOUN   PLURAL NOUN

MAD LIBS® is fun to play with friends, but you can also play it by yourself! To begin with, DO NOT look at the story on the page below. Fill in the blanks on this page with the words called for. Then, using the words you have selected, fill in the blank spaces in the story.

Now you've created your own hilarious MAD LIBS® game!

IRELAND

PLACE
_____

PLURAL NOUN
_____

ADJECTIVE
_____

PLURAL NOUN
_____

NOUN
_____

PLURAL NOUN
_____

PLURAL NOUN
_____

NOUN
_____

NOUN
_____

ANOTHER PLACE
_____

PLURAL NOUN
_____

PLURAL NOUN
_____

MAD LIBS®
IRELAND

Ireland is a beautiful green island lying directly west of _____.
_____PLACE_____

In 250 B.C., Ireland was inhabited by short, dark _____ who
_____PLURAL NOUN

were later called "Picts." They intermarried with _____ Vikings
_____ADJECTIVE

and with Celts who were _____ from Northern Europe.
_____PLURAL NOUN

In 1846, a blight ruined the _____ crop in Ireland, and
_____NOUN

over a million Irishmen migrated to the United States. Many of their

descendants have become very important American _____.
_____PLURAL NOUN

The Irish are noted for their poetry and songs. Some of these Irish

songs are: "When Irish _____ Are Smiling," "Did Your
_____PLURAL NOUN

_____ Come from Ireland?", and "McNamara's _____."
NOUN_____NOUN

Thousands of American tourists go to Ireland every year to visit its

capital, _____, and buy Irish linen _____
_____ANOTHER PLACE_____PLURAL NOUN

and see the beautiful _____ and lakes.
_____PLURAL NOUN

TARZAN

ADJECTIVE _____

PLURAL NOUN _____

ANIMAL _____

ADJECTIVE _____

PLACE _____

TYPE OF FOOD (PLURAL) _____

NOUN _____

FUNNY NOISE _____

ADJECTIVE _____

ANOTHER ANIMAL _____

ADJECTIVE _____

PLURAL NOUN _____

PERSON IN ROOM _____

MAD LIBS® is fun to play with friends, but you can also play it by yourself! To begin, DO NOT look at the story on the page below. Fill in the blanks on this page with the words called for. Then, using the words you have selected, fill in the blank spaces in the story.

Now you've created your own hilarious MAD LIBS® game!

MAD LIBS®

TARZAN

One of the most ____________ (ADJECTIVE) characters in fiction is called "Tarzan of the ____________ (PLURAL NOUN)." Tarzan was raised by a/an ____________ (ANIMAL) and lives in a/an ____________ (ADJECTIVE) jungle in the heart of darkest ____________ (PLACE). He spends most of his time eating ____________ (TYPE OF FOOD (PLURAL)) and swinging from tree to ____________ (NOUN). Whenever he gets angry, he beats on his chest and says, "____________ (FUNNY NOISE)!" This is his war cry. Tarzan always dresses in ____________ (ADJECTIVE) shorts made from the skin of a/an ____________ (ANOTHER ANIMAL), and his best friend is a/an ____________ (ADJECTIVE) chimpanzee named Cheetah. He is supposed to be able to speak to elephants and ____________ (PLURAL NOUN). In the movies, Tarzan is played by ____________ (PERSON IN ROOM).

MAD LIBS® is fun to play with friends, but you can also play it by yourself! To begin with, DO NOT look at the story on the page below. Fill in the blanks on this page with the words called for. Then, using the words you have selected, fill in the blank spaces in the story.

Now you've created your own hilarious MAD LIBS® game!

DOGS

NOUN _____

ADJECTIVE _____

ADJECTIVE _____

NOUN _____

NOUN _____

ADVERB _____

NOUN _____

NOUN _____

COLOR _____

ADJECTIVE _____

ADJECTIVE _____

NUMBER _____

ADJECTIVE _____

PLURAL NOUN _____

ADJECTIVE _____

NOUN _____

MAD LIBS®
DOGS

It has often been said that "a dog is man's best _____." Dogs
_____NOUN_____

are very _____ and can be taught many _____
_____ADJECTIVE_____ _____ADJECTIVE_____

tricks. A dog can be trained to carry a/an _____ in his mouth.
_____NOUN_____

And if you throw this _____, he will run and fetch it. Dogs
_____NOUN_____

will also bark _____ if someone tries to break into your
_____ADVERB_____

_____ during the night. One of the most popular canine pets
__NOUN__

today is the _____ spaniel. Spaniels have curly _____
_____NOUN_____ _____COLOR_____

coats and _____ ears. They also have very _____
_____ADJECTIVE_____ _____ADJECTIVE_____

dispositions and live to be _____ years old. Other popular dogs
_____NUMBER_____

are _____ terriers, German _____, and the
_____ADJECTIVE_____ _____PLURAL NOUN_____

_____ poodle. Every home should have a loyal dog for a/an
___ADJECTIVE___

_____.
____NOUN____

From GOOFY MAD LIBS® • Copyright © 2001, 1988 by Price Stern Sloan,
an imprint of Penguin Group (USA) Inc., 345 Hudson Street, New York, NY 10014.

WHAT TO DO WHEN YOU HAVE A COLD

NOUN _____

NOUN _____

PLURAL NOUN _____

NOUN _____

TYPE OF LIQUID _____

NOUN _____

NOUN _____

NOUN _____

NUMBER _____

NOUN _____

EXCLAMATION _____

NOUN _____

ADJECTIVE _____

ADJECTIVE _____

MAD LIBS®
WHAT TO DO WHEN YOU HAVE A COLD

You can always tell when you're getting a cold because your _____
                                                                NOUN

will feel stuffy and you will have a/an _____ -ache.
                                              NOUN

The first thing to do is to take a couple of _____ .
                                                    PLURAL NOUN

Then get into your _____ and rest, and drink plenty of
                          NOUN

_____ . Sometimes it's fun being sick. Food is brought
      TYPE OF LIQUID

to you on a/an _____ so you can eat and watch TV, and
                      NOUN

your temperature is taken by putting a/an _____ in your
                                                  NOUN

_____ . If you temperature goes over _____ degrees,
      NOUN   NUMBER

a doctor should be called. He will thump you on the _____
                                                          NOUN

and say, "_____!" Then he will ask you what _____
               EXCLAMATION   NOUN

you ate the night before and x-ray your stomach. Finally, he will give

you _____ advice on how to get well. If you do just what
         ADJECTIVE

he says, you'll feel _____ in no time at all.
                          ADJECTIVE

From GOOFY MAD LIBS® • Copyright © 2001, 1988 by Price Stern Sloan,
an imprint of Penguin Group (USA) Inc., 345 Hudson Street, New York, NY 10014.

MAD LIBS® is fun to play with friends, but you can also play it by yourself! To begin with, DO NOT look at the story on the page below. Fill in the blanks on this page with the words called for. Then, using the words you have selected, fill in the blank spaces in the story.

Now you've created your own hilarious MAD LIBS® game!

SPECIAL SPRING CLOTHING SALE

PERSON IN ROOM (MALE)_____

ADJECTIVE_____

CITY_____

ADJECTIVE_____

ADJECTIVE_____

ARTICLE OF CLOTHING (PLURAL)_____

PLURAL NOUN_____

PLURAL NOUN_____

PLURAL NOUN_____

COLOR_____

ADJECTIVE_____

ADJECTIVE_____

PLURAL NOUN_____

ADJECTIVE_____

MAD LIBS®
SPECIAL SPRING
CLOTHING SALE

_____ has announced that his _____ clothing
PERSON IN ROOM (MALE)   ADJECTIVE

store in the heart of downtown _____ is having a/an
                                            CITY

_____ sale of all merchandise, including _____ suits
ADJECTIVE   ADJECTIVE

and slightly irregular _____ . Men's cable-knit
                        ARTICLE OF CLOTHING (PLURAL)

_____ , only $15.99. Hand-woven Italian _____ , half-price.
PLURAL NOUN   PLURAL NOUN

Double-breasted cashmere _____ , $50.00. Genuine imported
                            PLURAL NOUN

_____ _____ shoes, _____ handkerchiefs,
COLOR   ADJECTIVE   ADJECTIVE

and women's embroidered _____ , all at rock-bottom prices.
                           PLURAL NOUN

This is a chance to get some really _____ bargains!
                                        ADJECTIVE

From GOOFY MAD LIBS® • Copyright © 2001, 1988 by Price Stern Sloan,
an imprint of Penguin Group (USA) Inc., 345 Hudson Street, New York, NY 10014.

MAD LIBS® is fun to play with friends, but you can also play it by yourself! To begin with, DO NOT look at the story on the page below. Fill in the blanks on this page with the words called for. Then, using the words you have selected, fill in the blank spaces in the story.

Now you've created your own hilarious MAD LIBS® game!

COMMERCIAL FOR FACE CREAM

PLURAL NOUN _____

NOUN _____

ADJECTIVE _____

NOUN _____

NOUN _____

ADJECTIVE _____

CELEBRITY _____

ADJECTIVE _____

PLURAL NOUN _____

ADJECTIVE _____

NOUN _____

NUMBER _____

NOUN _____

MAD LIBS®
COMMERCIAL FOR
FACE CREAM

And now, ladies and _____ , an important commercial
                      PLURAL NOUN

message from our _____ , the manufacturer of new, improved
                    NOUN

ALL-GOO, the face cream for women. ALL-GOO now contains a new

_____ ingredient called "Hexa-mone," which is made from
   ADJECTIVE

distilled _____ juice. If you rub ALL-GOO on your _____
            NOUN   NOUN

every evening, your complexion will look as _____ as a daisy.
                                              ADJECTIVE

The famous Hollywood star, _____ , says, "I use ALL-GOO
                              CELEBRITY

every day, and my complexion is always _____ and my
                                           ADJECTIVE

_____ always have a youthful glow." Yes, ALL-GOO is the
  PLURAL NOUN

_____ cream of the stars. Remember, if you want a softer,
   ADJECTIVE

smoother _____ , get ALL-GOO in the handy _____-
            NOUN   NUMBER

pound size at your friendly neighborhood _____ store.
                                            NOUN

PRIME-TIME MAD LIBS

by Roger Price & Leonard Stern

PSS!
PRICE STERN SLOAN
An Imprint of Penguin Group (USA) Inc.

PRICE STERN SLOAN
Penguin Group (USA) Inc., 375 Hudson Street, New York, New York 10014, USA
Penguin Group (Canada), 90 Eglinton Avenue East, Suite 700,
Toronto, Ontario M4P 2Y3, Canada (a division of Pearson Penguin Canada Inc.)
Penguin Books Ltd, 80 Strand, London WC2R 0RL, England
Penguin Ireland, 25 St Stephen's Green, Dublin 2, Ireland
(a division of Penguin Books Ltd)
Penguin Group (Australia), 707 Collins Street, Melbourne, Victoria 3008, Australia
(a division of Pearson Australia Group Pty Ltd)
Penguin Books India Pvt Ltd, 11 Community Centre,
Panchsheel Park, New Delhi—110 017, India
Penguin Group (NZ), 67 Apollo Drive, Rosedale, Auckland 0632, New Zealand
(a division of Pearson New Zealand Ltd)
Penguin Books, Rosebank Office Park, 181 Jan Smuts Avenue,
Parktown North 2193, South Africa
Penguin China, B7 Jiaming Center, 27 East Third Ring Road North,
Chaoyang District, Beijing 100020, China

Penguin Books Ltd, Registered Offices:
80 Strand, London WC2R 0RL, England

Published by Price Stern Sloan, a division of Penguin Young Readers Group,
345 Hudson Street, New York, New York 10014.

ISBN 0-8431-4886-1

MAD LIBS

INSTRUCTIONS

MAD LIBS® is a game for people who don't like games!
It can be played by one, two, three, four, or forty.

● RIDICULOUSLY SIMPLE DIRECTIONS

In this tablet you will find stories containing blank spaces where words are left out. One player, the READER, selects one of these stories. The READER does not tell anyone what the story is about. Instead, he/she asks the other players, the WRITERS, to give him/her words. These words are used to fill in the blank spaces in the story.

● TO PLAY

The READER asks each WRITER in turn to call out a word—an adjective or a noun or whatever the space calls for—and uses them to fill in the blank spaces in the story. The result is a MAD LIBS® game.

When the READER then reads the completed MAD LIBS® game to the other players, they will discover that they have written a story that is fantastic, screamingly funny, shocking, silly, crazy, or just plain dumb—depending upon which words each WRITER called out.

● EXAMPLE (*Before* and *After*)

"_____!" he said _____
      EXCLAMATION   ADVERB

as he jumped into his convertible _____ and
                                        NOUN

drove off with his _____ wife.
                      ADJECTIVE

"_____*Ouch*_____!" he said _____*stupidly*_____
      EXCLAMATION   ADVERB

as he jumped into his convertible _____*cat*_____ and
                                      NOUN

drove off with his _____*brave*_____ wife.
                      ADJECTIVE

In case you have forgotten what adjectives, adverbs, nouns, and verbs are, here is a quick review:

An ADJECTIVE describes something or somebody. *Lumpy*, *soft*, *ugly*, *messy*, and *short* are adjectives.

An ADVERB tells how something is done. It modifies a verb and usually ends in "ly." *Modestly*, *stupidly*, *greedily*, and *carefully* are adverbs.

A NOUN is the name of a person, place, or thing. *Sidewalk*, *umbrella*, *bridle*, *bathtub*, and *nose* are nouns.

A VERB is an action word. *Run*, *pitch*, *jump*, and *swim* are verbs. Put the verbs in past tense if the directions say PAST TENSE. *Ran*, *pitched*, *jumped*, and *swam* are verbs in the past tense.

When we ask for A PLACE, we mean any sort of place: a country or city (*Spain*, *Cleveland*) or a room (*bathroom*, *kitchen*).

An EXCLAMATION or SILLY WORD is any sort of funny sound, gasp, grunt, or outcry, like *Wow!*, *Ouch!*, *Whomp!*, *Ick!*, and *Gadzooks!*

When we ask for specific words, like a NUMBER, a COLOR, an ANIMAL, or a PART OF THE BODY, we mean a word that is one of those things, like *seven*, *blue*, *horse*, or *head*.

When we ask for a PLURAL, it means more than one. For example, *cat* pluralized is *cats*.

MAD LIBS® is fun to play with friends, but you can also play it by yourself! To begin with, DO NOT look at the story on the page below. Fill in the blanks on this page with the words called for. Then, using the words you have selected, fill in the blank spaces in the story.

Now you've created your own hilarious MAD LIBS® game!

VIEWING TIPS, PART ONE

_____ FIRST NAME (MALE)

_____ ADJECTIVE

_____ NOUN

_____ PART OF THE BODY

_____ PLURAL NOUN

_____ PLURAL NOUN

_____ ADJECTIVE

_____ PLURAL NOUN

_____ ADJECTIVE

_____ PLURAL NOUN

_____ ADJECTIVE

_____ LAST NAME OF PERSON

_____ NOUN

_____ ADJECTIVE

_____ ADJECTIVE

_____ OCCUPATION (PLURAL)

MAD LIBS®
VIEWING TIPS, PART ONE

Everybody Loves _____: Tonight we learn what
　　　　　　　　　FIRST NAME (MALE)

happens to a/an _____ husband when he forgets it's his
　　　　　　　　　ADJECTIVE

anniversary and invites his buddies over to the house for an all night poker

_____.
NOUN

Monday Night _____-*ball*: The New York _____
　　　　　　　PART OF THE BODY　　　　　　　　　　　　　PLURAL NOUN

play the St. Louis _____ in a game that will decide who
　　　　　　　　　　PLURAL NOUN

goes to the _____ Bowl.
　　　　　　　ADJECTIVE

60 _____: Investigates the _____ practice of
　　　PLURAL NOUN　　　　　　　　　　　　ADJECTIVE

laundering counterfeit _____ through _____ banks
　　　　　　　　　　　　PLURAL NOUN　　　　　　　　ADJECTIVE

in the _____ Islands.
　　　LAST NAME OF PERSON

State of the _____ speech: The president is scheduled to
　　　　　　　NOUN

deliver his _____ address before a/an _____
　　　　　　ADJECTIVE　　　　　　　　　　　　　　　ADJECTIVE

session of Congress, telecast from the House of _____.
　　　　　　　　　　　　　　　　　　　　　　　OCCUPATION (PLURAL)

From PRIME-TIME MAD LIBS® • Copyright © 2002 by Price Stern Sloan,
an imprint of Penguin Group (USA) Inc., 345 Hudson Street, New York, NY 10014.

MAD LIBS® is fun to play with friends, but you can also play it by yourself! To begin with, DO NOT look at the story on the page below. Fill in the blanks on this page with the words called for. Then, using the words you have selected, fill in the blank spaces in the story.

Now you've created your own hilarious MAD LIBS® game!

VIEWING TIPS, PART TWO

_____
NOUN

_____
PLURAL NOUN

_____
ADJECTIVE

_____
ADJECTIVE

_____
FIRST NAME (MALE)

_____
FIRST NAME (FEMALE)

_____
ADJECTIVE

_____
NUMBER

_____
NOUN

_____
PLURAL NOUN

_____
NOUN

_____
LAST NAME OF PERSON

_____
ADJECTIVE

_____
NOUN

_____
NOUN

_____
NOUN

MAD LIBS®
VIEWING TIPS,
PART TWO

Law and _____: The district attorney believes the
NOUN

sentences handed out to two _____ are _____. She
PLURAL NOUN   ADJECTIVE

convinces the _____ judge to change his verdict.
ADJECTIVE

_____ *and* _____: Living on a/an
FIRST NAME (MALE)   FIRST NAME (FEMALE)

_____ budget, our couple agree to limit spending on
ADJECTIVE

anniversary gifts to no more than _____ dollars. She keeps her
NUMBER

_____ and gives him a pair of wooden _____. He
NOUN   PLURAL NOUN

spends a fortune on a gold _____.
NOUN

Masterpiece Theater: Robinson _____. The
LAST NAME OF PERSON

_____ story of a shipwrecked _____ who befriends a
ADJECTIVE   NOUN

native _____ on a desert _____.
NOUN   NOUN

MAD LIBS® is fun to play with friends, but you can also play it by yourself! To begin with, DO NOT look at the story on the page below. Fill in the blanks on this page with the words called for. Then, using the words you have selected, fill in the blank spaces in the story.

Now you've created your own hilarious MAD LIBS® game!

PROMOS

FIRST NAME (MALE) _____

FIRST NAME (FEMALE) _____

NOUN _____

ARTICLE OF CLOTHING (PLURAL) _____

PART OF THE BODY _____

NOUN _____

PART OF THE BODY (PLURAL) _____

LAST NAME OF PERSON _____

ADJECTIVE _____

ADJECTIVE _____

PLURAL NOUN _____

NOUN _____

ADVERB _____

NOUN _____

ADVERB _____

ADJECTIVE _____

PLURAL NOUN _____

NOUN _____

MAD LIBS®
PROMOS

Newspaper critics agree that "_____ and
                                    FIRST NAME (MALE)

_____" is a comedy _____ that will knock
      FIRST NAME (FEMALE)   NOUN

your _____ off.
        ARTICLE OF CLOTHING (PLURAL)

"It will tickle your funny _____!"
                            PART OF THE BODY

                                        —*The Washington* _____
                                                              NOUN

"Two _____ up!"
        PART OF THE BODY (PLURAL)

                                    —Ebert and _____
                                                    LAST NAME OF PERSON

"A smart, _____, and _____ comedy. You not
              ADJECTIVE   ADJECTIVE

only laugh, but it brings _____ to your eyes."
                            PLURAL NOUN

                            —*The New Orleans Times-* _____
                                                            NOUN

"A/An _____ funny half-hour _____; _____
          ADVERB   NOUN   ADVERB

acted by a/an _____ cast of all-star _____."
                  ADJECTIVE   PLURAL NOUN

                            —*The Chicago Sun-* _____
                                                    NOUN

WORLD SERIES BROADCAST

NOUN _____

PLURAL NOUN _____

NUMBER _____

ANOTHER NUMBER _____

NOUN _____

PART OF THE BODY (PLURAL) _____

PLURAL NOUN _____

ADJECTIVE _____

LAST NAME OF PERSON _____

VERB _____

NOUN _____

NAME OF PERSON (MALE) _____

NOUN _____

NOUN _____

NOUN _____

NOUN _____

NUMBER _____

ADJECTIVE _____

ADJECTIVE _____

MAD LIBS®
WORLD SERIES BROADCAST

Hard to believe—no, impossible to believe! Here we are in the

bottom of the ninth _____, the score is tied, there are two
                         NOUN

outs, and the _____ are loaded . . . and yes, the count on the
                 PLURAL NOUN

batter is _____ and _____. What an
              NUMBER   ANOTHER NUMBER

unbelievable moment! There isn't a fan sitting in his or her _____.
                                                              NOUN

They're all standing on their _____, screaming
                               PART OF THE BODY (PLURAL)

at the top of their _____. Here comes the pitch. It's a ninety-
                     PLURAL NOUN

mile-an-hour _____ ball. Foul! _____ just
              ADJECTIVE   LAST NAME OF PERSON

managed to _____ the ball with the end of his _____.
             VERB   NOUN

_____ rubs up another _____, steps on the
NAME OF PERSON (MALE)   NOUN

_____ , and gets his _____ from the catcher squatting
  NOUN   NOUN

behind the _____. Here it comes . . . and there it goes! Ladies
             NOUN

and gentlemen, it's a _____-foot home run. Wow! What a/an
                        NUMBER

_____ ending to a truly _____ game.
  ADJECTIVE   ADJECTIVE

MAD LIBS® is fun to play with friends, but you can also play it by yourself! To begin with, DO NOT look at the story on the page below. Fill in the blanks on this page with the words called for. Then, using the words you have selected, fill in the blank spaces in the story.

Now you've created your own hilarious MAD LIBS® game!

MASTERPIECE THEATER

PERSON IN ROOM (FEMALE) _____

ADVERB _____

PLURAL NOUN _____

ADJECTIVE _____

OCCUPATION (PLURAL) _____

ADJECTIVE _____

ADJECTIVE _____

ADJECTIVE _____

ADJECTIVE _____

ADJECTIVE _____

PLURAL NOUN _____

ANOTHER OCCUPATION (PLURAL) _____

ARTICLE OF CLOTHING (PLURAL) _____

ANIMAL (PLURAL) _____

MAD LIBS®
MASTERPIECE THEATER

(To be read by _____)
PERSON IN ROOM (FEMALE)

No story ever told seems to _____ capture the hearts
ADVERB

and _____ of _____ readers as does the legend
PLURAL NOUN   ADJECTIVE

of King Arthur and the _____ of the _____
OCCUPATION (PLURAL)   ADJECTIVE

table. If we choose to believe the Arthur legend and go along with

the story that this _____ king removed from a/an _____
ADJECTIVE   ADJECTIVE

stone the _____ sword called Excalibur, then we are giving
ADJECTIVE

ourselves permission to enjoy this evening's performance. So

without further ado let us visit the kingdom of Camelot, where

_____ knights perform heroic _____, rescue
ADJECTIVE   PLURAL NOUN

_____ in distress, and, in _____
ANOTHER OCCUPATION (PLURAL)   ARTICLE OF CLOTHING (PLURAL)

of armor, ride off on majestic _____ in search of
ANIMAL (PLURAL)

adventure.

MAD LIBS® is fun to play with friends, but you can also play it by yourself! To begin with, DO NOT look at the story on the page below. Fill in the blanks on this page with the words called for. Then, using the words you have selected, fill in the blank spaces in the story.

Now you've created your own hilarious MAD LIBS® game!

EMMY ACCEPTANCE SPEECH

PART OF THE BODY _____

NOUN _____

ADJECTIVE _____

NAME OF PERSON (FEMALE) _____

OCCUPATION _____

VERB ENDING IN "ING" _____

ADJECTIVE _____

NAME OF PERSON (MALE) _____

ADJECTIVE _____

ANOTHER OCCUPATION _____

MAD LIBS®
EMMY ACCEPTANCE SPEECH

"Thank you! Thank you from the bottom of my _____.
                                              PART OF THE BODY

I don't know what to say. I'm speechless. I truly didn't expect to win

this _____, certainly not with so many _____ actors
         NOUN   ADJECTIVE

competing in the same category. First and foremost, my thanks to

_____. You couldn't work with a better
     NAME OF PERSON (FEMALE)

_____. And I'm sure I wouldn't be _____
   OCCUPATION   VERB ENDING IN "ING"

here tonight if it weren't for my _____ director. I must also
                                    ADJECTIVE

thank _____, who wrote a/an _____
        NAME OF PERSON (MALE)   ADJECTIVE

script for me. Of course, none of this would be happening if it

weren't for my agent, who convinced the network that I could play

a seventy-five-year-old, retired _____."
                                 ANOTHER OCCUPATION

MAD LIBS® is fun to play with friends, but you can also play it by yourself! To begin with, DO NOT look at the story on the page below. Fill in the blanks on this page with the words called for. Then, using the words you have selected, fill in the blank spaces in the story.

Now you've created your own hilarious MAD LIBS® game!

SCENE FROM A HIT SITCOM

NOUN _____

NOUN _____

ADJECTIVE _____

ROOM _____

ADJECTIVE _____

ADVERB _____

ARTICLE OF CLOTHING _____

ANIMAL (PLURAL) _____

ADJECTIVE _____

FIRST NAME (FEMALE) _____

VERB _____

FIRST NAME (MALE) _____

VERB _____

PLURAL NOUN _____

ADVERB _____

NOUN _____

ADVERB _____

NOUN _____

MAD LIBS®
SCENE FROM A HIT SITCOM

(Amy enters through the front _____, flops onto the overstuffed
NOUN

_____, and heaves a/an _____ sigh of exhaustion.
NOUN   ADJECTIVE

Jenny comes out of the _____.)
ROOM

JENNY: Hi! Did you have a/an _____ day?
ADJECTIVE

AMY: A/An _____ exhausting day. You're home early.
ADVERB

JENNY: Had to change my _____ before we go out.
ARTICLE OF CLOTHING

AMY: Go out? Wild _____ couldn't drag me out. I'm
ANIMAL (PLURAL)

really _____.
ADJECTIVE

JENNY: Oh, no, we're meeting _____ for a quick
FIRST NAME (FEMALE)

_____. She's finally bringing _____ to _____ you.
VERB   FIRST NAME (MALE)   VERB

AMY: No more blind _____ for me. Never again!
PLURAL NOUN

JENNY: But he's _____ your type—a self-made _____
ADVERB   NOUN

and _____ handsome.
ADVERB

AMY: Oh well, one more _____ can't hurt me.
NOUN

MAD LIBS® is fun to play with friends, but you can also play it by yourself! To begin with, DO NOT look at the story on the page below. Fill in the blanks on this page with the words called for. Then, using the words you have selected, fill in the blank spaces in the story.

Now you've created your own hilarious MAD LIBS® game!

LETTERS TO A TV EDITOR

PLURAL NOUN _____

ADJECTIVE _____

RELATIVE _____

ADJECTIVE _____

ADJECTIVE _____

NOUN _____

VERB _____

ADJECTIVE _____

ANIMAL (PLURAL) _____

NOUN _____

ADJECTIVE _____

VERB ENDING IN "ING" _____

NOUN _____

ADJECTIVE _____

PLURAL NOUN _____

ADJECTIVE _____

NOUN _____

TYPE OF VEGETABLE _____

MAD LIBS®
LETTERS TO A TV EDITOR

How dumb can network _____ be? They cancel a/an
                        PLURAL NOUN

_____ show such as *I'll Be a Monkey's* _____ and
ADJECTIVE   RELATIVE

replace it with another one of those _____ reality shows.
                                        ADJECTIVE

Why don't they take all those _____ TV executives, put
                                 ADJECTIVE

them on a desert _____, and leave them there to _____!
                    NOUN   VERB

Signed: A/An _____ Viewer
              ADJECTIVE

Believe me, television is going to the _____. I can't
                                         ANIMAL (PLURAL)

believe the _____ they're dishing out. What's being offered to
              NOUN

the _____ public is truly mind- _____ .
     ADJECTIVE   VERB ENDING IN "ING"

Signed: A Disenchanted _____
                          NOUN

I think today's sitcoms are just as _____ as the golden
                                       ADJECTIVE

_____ of the past. What needs to be eliminated is the
PLURAL NOUN

_____ laugh _____ .
ADJECTIVE   NOUN

Signed: A Confirmed Couch _____
                            TYPE OF VEGETABLE

From PRIME-TIME MAD LIBS® • Copyright © 2002 by Price Stern Sloan,
an imprint of Penguin Group (USA) Inc., 345 Hudson Street, New York, NY 10014.

COURTROOM DRAMA, PART ONE

NOUN _____

ADJECTIVE _____

NOUN _____

ADJECTIVE _____

NOUN _____

ADJECTIVE _____

FULL NAME _____

NOUN _____

ADJECTIVE _____

PART OF THE BODY (PLURAL) _____

NOUN _____

NOUN _____

ADJECTIVE _____

MAD LIBS
COURTROOM DRAMA, PART ONE

LAWYER: Your honor, I have discovered a witness who can prove, beyond a shadow of a _____, that my client is a/an

NOUN

_____ man.

ADJECTIVE

JUDGE: Call the _____.

NOUN

CLERK: Do you solemnly swear to tell the _____ truth and

ADJECTIVE

nothing but the _____?

NOUN

WITNESS: I do.

LAWYER: Please state your _____ name and occupation.

ADJECTIVE

WITNESS: (hard to understand) My name is _____ and I

FULL NAME

am a/an _____ driver.

NOUN

JUDGE: I can't understand you. What is wrong—are you _____?

ADJECTIVE

WITNESS: I forgot my false _____. They're in my

PART OF THE BODY (PLURAL)

car. (Laughter in the courtroom. Judge raps his _____ on

NOUN

his _____.)

NOUN

JUDGE: Order in the court. We'll have a ten-minute recess to allow

the witness to get his _____ teeth.

ADJECTIVE

From PRIME-TIME MAD LIBS® • Copyright © 2002 by Price Stern Sloan,
an imprint of Penguin Group (USA) Inc., 345 Hudson Street, New York, NY 10014.

MAD LIBS® is fun to play with friends, but you can also play it by yourself! To begin with, DO NOT look at the story on the page below. Fill in the blanks on this page with the words called for. Then, using the words you have selected, fill in the blank spaces in the story.

Now you've created your own hilarious MAD LIBS® game!

COURTROOM DRAMA, PART TWO

NOUN
_____

VERB ENDING IN "ING"
_____

NOUN
_____

PART OF THE BODY
_____

ADJECTIVE
_____

NOUN
_____

NOUN
_____

PART OF THE BODY
_____

ADVERB
_____

NOUN
_____

ADJECTIVE
_____

VERB ENDING IN "ING"
_____

MAD LIBS®
COURTROOM DRAMA, PART TWO

LAWYER: (to witness) As I understand, you actually saw the theft take place?

WITNESS: Yes, sir. I was in my _____ when this big guy comes

NOUN

_____ down the street. As he passes by, he grabs

VERB ENDING IN "ING"

this lady's _____ right out of her _____.

NOUN   PART OF THE BODY

LAWYER: Take a/an _____ look at the defendant. Is he the man

ADJECTIVE

you saw lift the lady's _____?

NOUN

WITNESS: No. The guy over there is the one who stole the _____.

NOUN

LAWYER: (shocked) What? Are you sure?

WITNESS: Yes, that's him. (Witness points at his _____.)

PART OF THE BODY

LAWYER: I apologize to the court. I _____ believed this man

ADVERB

was a credible _____.

NOUN

JUDGE: Strike the _____ testimony. Let's take another recess.

ADJECTIVE

I have a/an _____ headache.

VERB ENDING IN "ING"

CRITICS' CHOICE

ADJECTIVE _____

PLACE _____

ADJECTIVE _____

NOUN _____

NOUN _____

ADJECTIVE _____

ADJECTIVE _____

ADJECTIVE _____

PLURAL NOUN _____

ADJECTIVE _____

PLURAL NOUN _____

COLOR _____

ADJECTIVE _____

ADVERB _____

OCCUPATION (PLURAL) _____

NOUN _____

PLURAL NOUN _____

ADJECTIVE _____

LARGE NUMBER _____

NOUN _____

MAD LIBS®
CRITICS' CHOICE

(What's _____ in prime time)
ADJECTIVE

Survival: _____: Another of those _____ reality
PLACE   ADJECTIVE

shows. The audience would be much happier if there wasn't a single

_____ left on the island. I give it one _____.
NOUN   NOUN

_____ *Hollywood Stories*: This biography, filled with
ADJECTIVE

many _____ twists and _____ turns, will
ADJECTIVE   ADJECTIVE

please the many _____ of this _____ performer.
PLURAL NOUN   ADJECTIVE

I give it seven _____.
PLURAL NOUN

The _____ *House*: This is one of my all-time _____
COLOR   ADJECTIVE

shows. It's about the staff who _____ work behind the scenes
ADVERB

as _____. It has everything: _____,
OCCUPATION (PLURAL)   NOUN

_____, and even _____ romance. _____
PLURAL NOUN   ADJECTIVE   LARGE NUMBER

stars for this prime-time _____.
NOUN

MAD LIBS® is fun to play with friends, but you can also play it by yourself! To begin with, DO NOT look at the story on the page below. Fill in the blanks on this page with the words called for. Then, using the words you have selected, fill in the blank spaces in the story.

Now you've created your own hilarious MAD LIBS® game!

MEDICAL DRAMA

_____
NAME OF PERSON

_____
ANOTHER NAME OF PERSON

_____
ANOTHER NAME OF PERSON

_____
PART OF THE BODY

_____
NOUN

_____
ADVERB

_____
PART OF THE BODY

_____
NOUN

_____
VERB ENDING IN "S"

_____
NOUN

_____
NOUN

_____
NOUN

_____
NOUN

_____
NOUN

_____
ADJECTIVE

MAD LIBS

MEDICAL DRAMA

(starring _____ _____
NAME OF PERSON   ANOTHER NAME OF PERSON

    and _____)
        ANOTHER NAME OF PERSON

NURSE: Thank goodness you're here, doctor. A patient was just

brought in with a badly bruised _____ and a ruptured
                            PART OF THE BODY

_____. Unfortunately, Dr. Smith plans to operate _____.
NOUN   ADVERB

DOCTOR: We can't let him! Look at the way his _____
                                    PART OF THE BODY

is shaking.

NURSE: Uh-oh, he's putting a mask over his _____! Doctor,
                                NOUN

stop him before he _____ somebody.
               VERB ENDING IN "S"

DOCTOR: Smith, you can't operate on this _____! I forbid it.
                                NOUN

SMITH: How dare you say that to me? I'm your mentor. You're like a/an

_____ to me.
NOUN

DOCTOR: And you're like a/an _____ to me, but I can't risk the
                                NOUN

wrath of a/an _____ to satisfy your ego. Look in the mirror.
            NOUN

Would you trust that _____ to remove a/an _____ nail?
               NOUN   ADJECTIVE

From PRIME-TIME MAD LIBS® • Copyright © 2002 by Price Stern Sloan,
an imprint of Penguin Group (USA) Inc., 345 Hudson Street, New York, NY 10014.

EMERGENCY

NOUN BEGINNING WITH "S"
_____

LARGE NUMBER
_____

ADJECTIVE
_____

PLURAL NOUN
_____

ADJECTIVE
_____

VERB ENDING IN "ING"
_____

ADJECTIVE
_____

ADJECTIVE
_____

ANIMAL
_____

ADJECTIVE
_____

NOUN
_____

NOUN
_____

NOUN
_____

PLURAL NOUN
_____

ADJECTIVE
_____

NOUN
_____

ADJECTIVE
_____

ADJECTIVE
_____

NOUN
_____

MAD LIBS®

EMERGENCY

NOUN BEGINNING WITH "S"

ES, on the air for _____ years, is one of those _____
           LARGE NUMBER   ADJECTIVE

programs that has earned both critical _____ and
                                                  PLURAL NOUN

_____ ratings. Based on the best-_____ book
ADJECTIVE   VERB ENDING IN "ING"

of the same name, this _____ drama centers on _____
                            ADJECTIVE   ADJECTIVE

veterinarians in the emergency room of a Chicago cat and _____
                                                   ANIMAL

hospital. In the series, the overworked and _____ vets are the
                                        ADJECTIVE

unlikely heroes who make life-and-_____ decisions almost
                                       NOUN

every moment of every _____. The series has won seven
                              NOUN

Golden _____ Awards, received a remarkable twenty-one
                NOUN

Emmy _____, and has collected seven of those _____
         PLURAL NOUN   ADJECTIVE

statues. The cast has won five People's _____ Awards and has
                                     NOUN

been honored four _____ years in a row by the Actors
                        ADJECTIVE

Guild of America for a/an _____ ensemble performance
                            ADJECTIVE

in a prime-time _____.
                NOUN

From PRIME-TIME MAD LIBS® • Copyright © 2002 by Price Stern Sloan,
an imprint of Penguin Group (USA) Inc., 345 Hudson Street, New York, NY 10014.

MAD LIBS® is fun to play with friends, but you can also play it by yourself! To begin with, DO NOT look at the story on the page below. Fill in the blanks on this page with the words called for. Then, using the words you have selected, fill in the blank spaces in the story.

Now you've created your own hilarious MAD LIBS® game!

PRIME-TIME GOSSIP

_____ NAME OF PERSON (MALE)

_____ OCCUPATION

_____ ADJECTIVE

_____ NAME OF PERSON (FEMALE)

_____ PART OF THE BODY (PLURAL)

_____ ADVERB

_____ ADJECTIVE

_____ ADJECTIVE

_____ ADJECTIVE

_____ ADJECTIVE

_____ NOUN

_____ CELEBRITY (MALE)

_____ PERSON IN ROOM (FEMALE)

_____ ADJECTIVE

_____ PLURAL NOUN

_____ PART OF THE BODY (PLURAL)

_____ PLURAL NOUN

MAD LIBS®
PRIME-TIME GOSSIP

Handsome _____ and his co-_____,
NAME OF PERSON (MALE)   OCCUPATION

the _____ _____ raised _____
     ADJECTIVE   NAME OF PERSON (FEMALE)   PART OF THE BODY (PLURAL)

when they were seen kissing _____ at the screening of their
                                    ADVERB

_____ TV movie. The _____ couple deny it's a
   ADJECTIVE   ADJECTIVE

romance; they say they are just _____ friends.
                                    ADJECTIVE

Here's another _____ tidbit—love must be in the _____.
                  ADJECTIVE   NOUN

_____ and _____ who had only _____
CELEBRITY (MALE)   PERSON IN ROOM (FEMALE)   ADJECTIVE

words for each other last week, were seen holding _____
                                                      PLURAL NOUN

and whispering in each other's _____ at this
                                    PART OF THE BODY (PLURAL)

week's benefit for adopted _____.
                              PLURAL NOUN

MAD LIBS® is fun to play with friends, but you can also play it by yourself! To begin with, DO NOT look at the story on the page below. Fill in the blanks on this page with the words called for. Then, using the words you have selected, fill in the blank spaces in the story.

Now you've created your own hilarious MAD LIBS® game!

MORE PRIME-TIME GOSSIP

_____ ADJECTIVE

_____ PLACE

_____ ADJECTIVE

_____ NOUN

_____ PLURAL NOUN

_____ PLURAL NOUN

_____ ADJECTIVE

_____ ADJECTIVE

_____ NOUN

_____ ADVERB

_____ PART OF THE BODY

_____ ADJECTIVE

_____ ARTICLE OF CLOTHING

_____ OCCUPATION (PLURAL)

_____ PART OF THE BODY (PLURAL)

MAD LIBS®
MORE PRIME-TIME GOSSIP

The ever- _____ _Gilligan's_ _____ looks as though it
        ADJECTIVE   PLACE

will end up as a/an _____ feature _____ . Both
                      ADJECTIVE   NOUN

Universal _____ and Paramount _____ are
            PLURAL NOUN   PLURAL NOUN

competing to turn this _____ comedy into a/an
                          ADJECTIVE

_____ blockbuster.
  ADJECTIVE

What world-famous _____ designer is _____ tearing
                      NOUN   ADVERB

his _____ out? His staff sold the same provocative and
      PART OF THE BODY

_____ low-cut _____ to two of TV's
  ADJECTIVE   ARTICLE OF CLOTHING

leading _____ . The women hate each other's
          OCCUPATION (PLURAL)

_____ .
  PART OF THE BODY (PLURAL)

From PRIME-TIME MAD LIBS® • Copyright © 2002 by Price Stern Sloan,
an imprint of Penguin Group (USA) Inc., 345 Hudson Street, New York, NY 10014.

MAD LIBS® is fun to play with friends, but you can also play it by yourself! To begin with, DO NOT look at the story on the page below. Fill in the blanks on this page with the words called for. Then, using the words you have selected, fill in the blank spaces in the story.

Now you've created your own hilarious MAD LIBS® game!

INTERVIEW WITH TV HUNK,

_____
NAME OF PERSON (MALE)

_____
ADJECTIVE

_____
OCCUPATION

_____
VERB ENDING IN "ING"

_____
ADJECTIVE

_____
LETTER OF THE ALPHABET

_____
ADJECTIVE

_____
VERB

_____
PLURAL NOUN

_____
ARTICLE OF CLOTHING

_____
PLURAL NOUN

_____
ADJECTIVE

_____
ADJECTIVE

MAD☺LIBS®
INTERVIEW WITH TV HUNK,
NAME OF PERSON (MALE)

INTERVIEWER: Getting right to it, how does it feel to be TV's leading sex symbol?

HUNK: Strange. I don't really notice it. Off-screen I'm really a/an
_____ person.
ADJECTIVE

INTERVIEWER: When did you decide you wanted to be a/an
_____?
OCCUPATION

HUNK: I was in a school production of *Hamlet*, and I received a/an

_____ ovation. That did it.
VERB ENDING IN "ING"

INTERVIEWER: Were you a/an _____ student in school?
ADJECTIVE

HUNK: I was a/an _____ student.
LETTER OF THE ALPHABET

INTERVIEWER: I understand you are a/an _____ reader. Care
ADJECTIVE

to _____ your favorites?
VERB

HUNK: Dickens's *Tale of Two* _____, and Dumas's *Man in*
PLURAL NOUN

the Iron _____.
ARTICLE OF CLOTHING

INTERVIEWER: How would you like your _____ to remember you?
PLURAL NOUN

HUNK: As a/an _____ actor and a/an _____ person.
ADJECTIVE   ADJECTIVE

From PRIME-TIME MAD LIBS® • Copyright © 2002 by Price Stern Sloan,
an imprint of Penguin Group (USA) Inc., 345 Hudson Street, New York, NY 10014.

MAD LIBS® is fun to play with friends, but you can also play it by yourself! To begin with, DO NOT look at the story on the page below. Fill in the blanks on this page with the words called for. Then, using the words you have selected, fill in the blank spaces in the story.

Now you've created your own hilarious MAD LIBS® game!

TV CELEBRITY MAGAZINE PIECE

PART OF THE BODY
_____

NAME OF PERSON (FEMALE)
_____

NOUN
_____

NOUN
_____

PART OF THE BODY
_____

NOUN
_____

PLURAL NOUN
_____

ADJECTIVE
_____

PART OF THE BODY
_____

NOUN
_____

PLURAL NOUN
_____

NOUN
_____

ADVERB
_____

ADVERB
_____

NOUN
_____

PART OF THE BODY (PLURAL)
_____

MAD LIBS®
TV CELEBRITY
MAGAZINE PIECE

Breathless, wearing her glasses on top of her _____,

PART OF THE BODY

_____ rushes into her dressing room on the

NAME OF PERSON (FEMALE)

set of *One* _____ *to Love.* She's wearing a colorful

NOUN

_____ around her _____, a full-length _____,

NOUN PART OF THE BODY NOUN

and very cool _____. Off-screen as well as on, she's

PLURAL NOUN

independent and _____ and very comfortable in her own

ADJECTIVE

_____. You understand immediately why she's a role

PART OF THE BODY

_____ for millions of teenage _____. Although

NOUN PLURAL NOUN

she's rehearsing her _____, she still finds time to _____

NOUN ADVERB

talk to us. But before we get far, she's called to the set. The interview

ends _____. Before leaving, she turns and says, "Just because

ADVERB

you're thought of as a/an _____ symbol doesn't mean you

NOUN

don't have a good head on your _____."

PART OF THE BODY (PLURAL)

MAD LIBS® is fun to play with friends, but you can also play it by yourself! To begin with, DO NOT look at the story on the page below. Fill in the blanks on this page with the words called for. Then, using the words you have selected, fill in the blank spaces in the story.

Now you've created your own hilarious MAD LIBS® game!

NEWSBREAK

NOUN _____

PLURAL NOUN _____

ADJECTIVE _____

VERB _____

ADJECTIVE _____

PLACE _____

ANIMAL _____

ADJECTIVE _____

PART OF THE BODY _____

TYPE OF FOOD _____

SAME ANIMAL _____

VERB (PAST TENSE) _____

NAME OF PERSON (MALE) _____

NUMBER _____

PLURAL NOUN _____

PLURAL NOUN _____

MAD LIBS®
NEWSBREAK

The president passed his physical _____ with flying
NOUN

_____ this morning. Doctors gave him a/an _____
PLURAL NOUN   ADJECTIVE

bill of health, but advised him to _____ at least twenty
VERB

minutes a day and to eat less _____ food.
ADJECTIVE

At the _____ zoo, a five-hundred pound _____ reached
PLACE   ANIMAL

out and grabbed a woman's _____ camera right out of her
ADJECTIVE

_____ when she tried to take his picture eating a/an
PART OF THE BODY

_____ . The _____ then _____
TYPE OF FOOD   SAME ANIMAL   VERB (PAST TENSE)

the camera.

Sometimes it doesn't pay to diet. Popular comedian

_____ , who's lost more than _____ pounds,
NAME OF PERSON (MALE)   NUMBER

was virtually caught with his _____ down when his
PLURAL NOUN

pants fell to the floor as he performed in front of an audience of five

hundred enthusiastic _____ .
PLURAL NOUN

MAD LIBS® is fun to play with friends, but you can also play it by yourself! To begin with, DO NOT look at the story on the page below. Fill in the blanks on this page with the words called for. Then, using the words you have selected, fill in the blank spaces in the story.

Now you've created your own hilarious MAD LIBS® game!

BREAKING WEATHER REPORT

_____ ADJECTIVE

_____ ADJECTIVE

_____ FIRST NAME (FEMALE)

_____ PLURAL NOUN

_____ NUMBER

_____ ADVERB

_____ ADJECTIVE

_____ ADJECTIVE

_____ NOUN

_____ PLURAL NOUN

_____ PLURAL NOUN

_____ VERB ENDING IN "ING"

_____ PLURAL NOUN

_____ NOUN

_____ VERB ENDING IN "ING"

_____ NOUN

_____ NOUN

_____ PLURAL NOUN

_____ NOUN

_____ NOUN

MAD LIBS®

BREAKING WEATHER REPORT

(to be read dramatically)

"We interrupt this _____ broadcast to bring you a/an
                    ADJECTIVE

_____ news bulletin. Hurricane _____,
ADJECTIVE   FIRST NAME (FEMALE)

with gusting _____ clocked at _____ miles an hour,
             PLURAL NOUN   NUMBER

is hammering the _____ populated Florida coast. This
                 ADVERB

_____ storm has left _____ devastation in its wake.
ADJECTIVE   ADJECTIVE

The National _____ Bureau reports that in Miami windows
             NOUN

have been blown out of fifty high-rise _____, showering the
                                        PLURAL NOUN

streets below with pieces of broken _____. The howling
                                     PLURAL NOUN

winds have reduced a newly built _____ center to
                                  VERB ENDING IN "ING"

_____. Police report a seven-ton railroad _____ was
PLURAL NOUN   NOUN

lifted off its track and sent _____ into a three-story
                               VERB ENDING IN "ING"

_____. Fortunately, there have been no casualties. Nevertheless, the
NOUN

governor has declared a/an _____ of emergency and advised all
                           NOUN

_____ to seek safety in a/an _____ shelter. And now
PLURAL NOUN   NOUN

back to your _____ in progress."
             NOUN

MAD LIBS® is fun to play with friends, but you can also play it by yourself! To begin with, DO NOT look at the story on the page below. Fill in the blanks on this page with the words called for. Then, using the words you have selected, fill in the blank spaces in the story.

Now you've created your own hilarious MAD LIBS® game!

COOKING WITH CHEF

_____ FIRST NAME

_____ VERB

_____ ADJECTIVE

_____ ADJECTIVE

_____ TYPE OF LIQUID

_____ ADJECTIVE

_____ PERIOD OF TIME

_____ ADJECTIVE

_____ PLURAL NOUN

_____ VERB

_____ ADJECTIVE

_____ ADJECTIVE

_____ TYPE OF CONTAINER

_____ TYPE OF FOOD (PLURAL)

_____ NOUN

_____ ADJECTIVE

_____ NOUN

_____ NOUN

_____ PART OF THE BODY

MAD LIBS®
COOKING WITH CHEF _____

You know what we're going to _____ today? A/An
VERB
_____ favorite of mine—a crab salad with fennel and
ADJECTIVE
_____ onions. To speed things along, I've already boiled
ADJECTIVE
a gallon of _____, added 1/4 cup of _____ salt, and
TYPE OF LIQUID   ADJECTIVE
dropped in the crabs and cooked them for _____. Now
PERIOD OF TIME
that they are _____, I will crack them into little
ADJECTIVE
_____. Next we have to _____ the onions and the fennel
PLURAL NOUN   VERB
until they are _____. To make the salad, we put the
ADJECTIVE
_____ crabs into a large _____ and add the
ADJECTIVE   TYPE OF CONTAINER
fennel, the onion, and a hefty portion of _____.
TYPE OF FOOD (PLURAL)
To dress the salad, sprinkle it with _____ oil, a touch of
NOUN
_____ lemon juice, and a pinch of _____ and
ADJECTIVE   NOUN
pepper. Okay, let's toss this _____ and taste it. Yum . . . delicious!
NOUN
A winner! A salad guaranteed to make your _____ water!
PART OF THE BODY

From PRIME-TIME MAD LIBS® • Copyright © 2002 by Price Stern Sloan,
an imprint of Penguin Group (USA) Inc., 345 Hudson Street, New York, NY 10014.

MAD LIBS® is fun to play with friends, but you can also play it by yourself! To begin with, DO NOT look at the story on the page below. Fill in the blanks on this page with the words called for. Then, using the words you have selected, fill in the blank spaces in the story.

Now you've created your own hilarious MAD LIBS® game!

CHATTING WITH A TEEN IDOL

_____
PERSON IN ROOM

_____
ANOTHER PERSON IN ROOM

_____
ADJECTIVE

_____
ADJECTIVE

_____
VERB

_____
OCCUPATION

_____
PART OF THE BODY

_____
VERB ENDING IN "ING"

_____
ANIMAL

_____
NUMBER

_____
ADJECTIVE

_____
ADJECTIVE

_____
VERB ENDING IN "ING"

_____
PART OF THE BODY

_____
ADJECTIVE

_____
VERB

_____
ADJECTIVE

MAD LIBS®
CHATTING WITH A TEEN IDOL

(as performed by _____ and _____)
PERSON IN ROOM   ANOTHER PERSON IN ROOM

INTERVIEWER: Wow! Those were some really _____ dance
ADJECTIVE

steps. I didn't realize you were that _____ a dancer. Where
ADJECTIVE

did you learn to _____?
VERB

TEEN IDOL: My mom taught me. She was a chorus _____.
OCCUPATION

INTERVIEWER: Are you going to _____-sync your
PART OF THE BODY

songs on this special?

TEEN IDOL: No. I gave up lip-_____ in my Mickey
VERB ENDING IN "ING"

_____ days. I can sing for _____ hours now.
ANIMAL   NUMBER

INTERVIEWER: You're really on a roll. You have this _____
ADJECTIVE

special and then you're off to make a/an _____ motion picture.
ADJECTIVE

TEEN IDOL: Yes. It's cool, really mind-_____! But I
VERB ENDING IN "ING"

promise I won't let it go to my _____.
PART OF THE BODY

INTERVIEWER: Is there anyone _____ in your life now?
ADJECTIVE

TEEN IDOL: No, I don't even have the time to _____. So I just
VERB

hang out with _____ friends now.
ADJECTIVE

UPSIDE-DOWN MAD LIBS

by Roger Price & Leonard Stern

PSS!

PRICE STERN SLOAN

An Imprint of Penguin Group (USA) Inc.

PRICE STERN SLOAN
Penguin Group (USA) Inc., 375 Hudson Street, New York, New York 10014, USA
Penguin Group (Canada), 90 Eglinton Avenue East, Suite 700,
Toronto, Ontario M4P 2Y3, Canada (a division of Pearson Penguin Canada Inc.)
Penguin Books Ltd, 80 Strand, London WC2R 0RL, England
Penguin Ireland, 25 St Stephen's Green, Dublin 2, Ireland
(a division of Penguin Books Ltd)
Penguin Group (Australia), 707 Collins Street, Melbourne, Victoria 3008, Australia
(a division of Pearson Australia Group Pty Ltd)
Penguin Books India Pvt Ltd, 11 Community Centre,
Panchsheel Park, New Delhi—110 017, India
Penguin Group (NZ), 67 Apollo Drive, Rosedale, Auckland 0632, New Zealand
(a division of Pearson New Zealand Ltd)
Penguin Books, Rosebank Office Park, 181 Jan Smuts Avenue,
Parktown North 2193, South Africa
Penguin China, B7 Jaiming Center, 27 East Third Ring Road North,
Chaoyang District, Beijing 100020, China

Penguin Books Ltd, Registered Offices:
80 Strand, London WC2R 0RL, England

Published by Price Stern Sloan, a division of Penguin Young Readers Group,
345 Hudson Street, New York, New York 10014.

ISBN 0-8431-3935-8

MAD LIBS®
INSTRUCTIONS

MAD LIBS® is a game for people who don't like games!
It can be played by one, two, three, four, or forty.

• RIDICULOUSLY SIMPLE DIRECTIONS

In this tablet you will find stories containing blank spaces where words are left out. One player, the READER, selects one of these stories. The READER does not tell anyone what the story is about. Instead, he/she asks the other players, the WRITERS, to give him/her words. These words are used to fill in the blank spaces in the story.

• TO PLAY

The READER asks each WRITER in turn to call out a word—an adjective or a noun or whatever the space calls for—and uses them to fill in the blank spaces in the story. The result is a MAD LIBS® game.

When the READER then reads the completed MAD LIBS® game to the other players, they will discover that they have written a story that is fantastic, screamingly funny, shocking, silly, crazy, or just plain dumb—depending upon which words each WRITER called out.

• EXAMPLE (*Before* and *After*)

"_____!" he said _____
　　　　　EXCLAMATION　　　　　　　　　　　　　　ADVERB

as he jumped into his convertible _____ and
　　　　　　　　　　　　　　　　　　　　　NOUN

drove off with his _____ wife.
　　　　　　　　　　　ADJECTIVE

"_____*Ouch*_____!" he said _____*stupidly*_____
　　　　EXCLAMATION　　　　　　　　　　ADVERB

as he jumped into his convertible _____*cat*_____ and
　　　　　　　　　　　　　　　　　　NOUN

drove off with his _____*brave*_____ wife.
　　　　　　　　　　ADJECTIVE

In case you have forgotten what adjectives, adverbs, nouns, and verbs are, here is a quick review:

An ADJECTIVE describes something or somebody. *Lumpy*, *soft*, *ugly*, *messy*, and *short* are adjectives.

An ADVERB tells how something is done. It modifies a verb and usually ends in "ly." *Modestly*, *stupidly*, *greedily*, and *carefully* are adverbs.

A NOUN is the name of a person, place, or thing. *Sidewalk*, *umbrella*, *bridle*, *bathtub*, and *nose* are nouns.

A VERB is an action word. *Run*, *pitch*, *jump*, and *swim* are verbs. Put the verbs in past tense if the directions say PAST TENSE. *Ran*, *pitched*, *jumped*, and *swam* are verbs in the past tense.

When we ask for A PLACE, we mean any sort of place: a country or city (*Spain*, *Cleveland*) or a room (*bathroom*, *kitchen*).

An EXCLAMATION or SILLY WORD is any sort of funny sound, gasp, grunt, or outcry, like *Wow!*, *Ouch!*, *Whomp!*, *Ick!*, and *Gadzooks!*

When we ask for specific words, like a NUMBER, a COLOR, an ANIMAL, or a PART OF THE BODY, we mean a word that is one of those things, like *seven*, *blue*, *horse*, or *head*.

When we ask for a PLURAL, it means more than one. For example, *cat* pluralized is *cats*.

MAD LIBS® is fun to play with friends, but you can also play it by yourself! To begin with, DO NOT look at the story on the page below. Fill in the blanks on this page with the words called for. Then, using the words you have selected, fill in the blank spaces in the story.

Now you've created your own hilarious MAD LIBS® game!

RECIPE FOR
AN UPSIDE-DOWN CAKE

_____
ADJECTIVE

_____
NOUN

_____
NOUN

_____
NUMBER

_____
NOUN

_____
ADJECTIVE

_____
ADJECTIVE

_____
ADJECTIVE

_____
VERB

_____
NOUN

_____
ADVERB

_____
PLURAL NOUN

_____
NOUN

_____
NOUN

_____
VERB

_____
NOUN

_____
ADJECTIVE

_____
VERB (PAST TENSE)

_____
NOUN

MAD LIBS®
RECIPE FOR
AN UPSIDE-DOWN CAKE

Here is a/an _____ recipe for an Upside-Down _____.
ADJECTIVE   NOUN

First, you preheat your _____ to _____ degrees. Then
                        NOUN   NUMBER

take a stick of _____ and melt it in a ten-inch _____
                NOUN   ADJECTIVE

skillet over a very _____ flame. In a/an _____ bowl
                    ADJECTIVE   ADJECTIVE

_____ granulated _____ and flour, stirring the mixture
VERB   NOUN

_____. Add milk and _____ and beat rapidly with
ADVERB   PLURAL NOUN

an electric _____. Bake until your _____ is ready.
            NOUN   NOUN

After the cake cools, _____ it from the _____
                      VERB   NOUN

and turn it upside-_____. Serve the cake warm with
                   ADJECTIVE

_____ cream and small spoonfuls of _____ on top.
VERB (PAST TENSE)   NOUN

MAD LIBS® is fun to play with friends, but you can also play it by yourself! To begin with, DO NOT look at the story on the page below. Fill in the blanks on this page with the words called for. Then, using the words you have selected, fill in the blank spaces in the story.

Now you've created your own hilarious MAD LIBS® game!

ALICE'S UPSIDE-DOWN WORLD

ADJECTIVE _____

NOUN _____

PLURAL NOUN _____

NUMBER _____

ADJECTIVE _____

VERB ENDING IN "S" _____

ADJECTIVE _____

NOUN _____

NOUN _____

NOUN _____

NOUN _____

VERB ENDING IN "S" _____

NOUN _____

ADJECTIVE _____

NOUN _____

PLURAL NOUN _____

ADJECTIVE _____

NOUN _____

MAD LIBS®
ALICE'S UPSIDE-DOWN WORLD

Lewis Carroll's classic, *Alice's Adventures in Wonderland*, as well as

its _____ sequel, *Through the Looking* _____,
      ADJECTIVE   NOUN

have enchanted both the young and the old _____ for the
                                              PLURAL NOUN

last _____ years. Alice's _____ adventures begin when
      NUMBER   ADJECTIVE

she _____ down a/an _____ hole and lands
     VERB ENDING IN "S"   ADJECTIVE

in a strange and topsy-turvy _____. There she discovers she
                                  NOUN

can become a tall _____ or a small _____ simply by
                      NOUN   NOUN

nibbling on alternate sides of a magic _____. In her travels
                                            NOUN

through Wonderland, Alice _____ such remarkable
                              VERB ENDING IN "S"

characters as the White _____, the _____ Hatter,
                            NOUN   ADJECTIVE

the Cheshire _____, and even the Queen of _____.
                 NOUN   PLURAL NOUN

Unfortunately, Alice's adventures come to a/an _____ end
                                                    ADJECTIVE

when Alice awakens from her _____.
                                NOUN

MAD LIBS® is fun to play with friends, but you can also play it by yourself! To begin with, DO NOT look at the story on the page below. Fill in the blanks on this page with the words called for. Then, using the words you have selected, fill in the blank spaces in the story.

Now you've created your own hilarious MAD LIBS® game!

EAT, DRINK, AND BE SICK

_____ NOUN

_____ ADJECTIVE

_____ ADJECTIVE

_____ NOUN

_____ NOUN

_____ PLURAL NOUN

_____ PLURAL NOUN

_____ NOUN

_____ PART OF THE BODY

_____ PLURAL NOUN

_____ ADVERB

_____ PLURAL NOUN

_____ PLURAL NOUN

_____ PLURAL NOUN

_____ LETTER OF THE ALPHABET

MAD LIBS

EAT, DRINK, AND BE SICK

An inspector from the Department of Health and _____ Services
_____NOUN

paid a surprise visit to our _____ school cafeteria. The lunch
_____ADJECTIVE

special, prepared by our _____ dietician, was spaghetti and
_____ADJECTIVE

_____-balls with a choice of either a/an _____ salad or
NOUN_____NOUN

french _____. The inspector found the meat-_____
_____PLURAL NOUN_____PLURAL NOUN

to be overcooked and discovered a live _____ in the fries,
_____NOUN

causing him to have a/an _____-ache. In response, he
_____PART OF THE BODY

threw up all over his _____. In his report, the inspector
_____PLURAL NOUN

_____ recommended that the school cafeteria serve only
_____ADVERB

nutritious _____ as well as low-calorie _____, and
_____PLURAL NOUN_____PLURAL NOUN

that all of the saturated _____ be eliminated. He rated the
_____PLURAL NOUN

cafeteria a/an _____-minus.
_____LETTER OF THE ALPHABET

MAD LIBS® is fun to play with friends, but you can also play it by yourself! To begin with, DO NOT look at the story on the page below. Fill in the blanks on this page with the words called for. Then, using the words you have selected, fill in the blank spaces in the story.

Now you've created your own hilarious MAD LIBS® game!

THE OBSERVATORY

ADJECTIVE _____

NOUN _____

NOUN _____

NOUN _____

NOUN _____

PLURAL NOUN _____

PLURAL NOUN _____

VERB _____

PLURAL NOUN _____

PLURAL NOUN _____

NOUN _____

NOUN _____

ADJECTIVE _____

VERB _____

NOUN _____

MAD LIBS®
THE OBSERVATORY

Our class went on a field trip to a/an _____ observatory.
                                        ADJECTIVE

It was located on top of a/an _____, and it looked like a giant
                                  NOUN

_____ with a slit down its _____. We went inside
      NOUN   NOUN

and looked through a/an _____ and were able to see
                                NOUN

_____ in the sky that were millions of _____
   PLURAL NOUN   PLURAL NOUN

away. The men and women who _____ in the observa-
                                     VERB

tory are called _____, and they are always watching for
                    PLURAL NOUN

comets, eclipses, and shooting _____. An eclipse occurs
                                     PLURAL NOUN

when a/a _____ comes between the earth and the _____
              NOUN   NOUN

and everything gets _____. Next week, we plan to
                            ADJECTIVE

_____ the Museum of Modern _____.
      VERB   NOUN

MAD LIBS® is fun to play with friends, but you can also play it by yourself! To begin with, DO NOT look at the story on the page below. Fill in the blanks on this page with the words called for. Then, using the words you have selected, fill in the blank spaces in the story.

Now you've created your own hilarious MAD LIBS® game!

UPSIDE-DOWN DICTIONARY STARTING WITH LETTER *A*

ADJECTIVE_____

PLURAL NOUN_____

ADJECTIVE_____

NOUN_____

NOUN_____

NOUN_____

ADJECTIVE_____

ADVERB_____

NOUN_____

PART OF THE BODY_____

ADJECTIVE_____

NOUN_____

NOUN_____

NOUN_____

AARDVARK (noun): A/An _____ mammal who feeds on ants
ADJECTIVE

and _____ . The aardvark is squat and has a/an _____
PLURAL NOUN   ADJECTIVE

tongue and a long _____ ending in a round, piglike _____
NOUN   NOUN

ANGEL (noun): A supernatural _____, either good or
NOUN

_____ , who is _____ seen as a white-robed
ADJECTIVE   ADVERB

_____ with wings over his or her _____
NOUN   PART OF THE BODY

ASTRONAUT (noun): Sometimes a/an _____ scientist, but
ADJECTIVE

usually an army or navy _____ trained to make flights to
NOUN

the _____ in a space _____
NOUN   NOUN

MAD LIBS® is fun to play with friends, but you can also play it by yourself! To begin with, DO NOT look at the story on the page below. Fill in the blanks on this page with the words called for. Then, using the words you have selected, fill in the blank spaces in the story.

Now you've created your own hilarious MAD LIBS® game!

CAR OF THE YEAR

PERSON IN ROOM (LAST NAME)_____

NOUN_____

NOUN_____

PLURAL NOUN_____

PLURAL NOUN_____

PLURAL NOUN_____

PLURAL NOUN_____

TYPE OF LIQUID_____

NOUN_____

VERB_____

SAME LAST NAME_____

PART OF THE BODY (PLURAL)_____

NOUN_____

ADJECTIVE_____

NOUN_____

EXCLAMATION_____

It's here, the all-new _____ . The most luxurious
<u>PERSON IN ROOM (LAST NAME)</u>

_____ you'll ever drive! The only four-door _____ that
<u>NOUN</u>   <u>NOUN</u>

comes equipped with dual air _____ , power _____ ,
<u>PLURAL NOUN</u>   <u>PLURAL NOUN</u>

and contoured, plush leather _____ . And, believe it or not,
<u>PLURAL NOUN</u>

it is the only car in its class that can go up to a hundred thousand

_____ without needing a/an _____ change or
<u>PLURAL NOUN</u>   <u>TYPE OF LIQUID</u>

a/an _____ tune-up. Run, do not _____ to your nearest
<u>NOUN</u>   <u>VERB</u>

_____ dealer and feast your _____ on
<u>SAME LAST NAME</u>   <u>PART OF THE BODY (PLURAL)</u>

the car that *Motor* _____ magazine calls the _____
<u>NOUN</u>   <u>ADJECTIVE</u>

_____ of the year. As always, we save the best for last: When
<u>NOUN</u>

you see the sticker price, you are sure to shout, "_____ !"
<u>EXCLAMATION</u>

MAD LIBS® is fun to play with friends, but you can also play it by yourself! To begin with, DO NOT look at the story on the page below. Fill in the blanks on this page with the words called for. Then, using the words you have selected, fill in the blank spaces in the story.

Now you've created your own hilarious MAD LIBS® game!

GREAT EXCUSES
FOR BEING LATE

_____ ADJECTIVE

_____ PERSON IN ROOM

_____ VERB ENDING IN "ING"

_____ PART OF THE BODY

_____ NOUN

_____ NOUN

_____ NUMBER

_____ PLURAL NOUN

_____ TYPE OF LIQUID

_____ ADVERB

_____ ANOTHER PERSON IN ROOM

_____ ADJECTIVE

_____ ADJECTIVE

_____ SAME PERSON IN ROOM

_____ ADJECTIVE

_____ ADJECTIVE

_____ ADJECTIVE

_____ PLURAL NOUN

_____ NOUN

_____ PLURAL NOUN

_____ VERB

_____ PLURAL NOUN

MAD LIBS®
GREAT EXCUSES
FOR BEING LATE

Dear Physical Education Teacher,

Please excuse my son/daughter from missing _____ class
                                              ADJECTIVE

yesterday. When _____ awakened yesterday, I could
                   PERSON IN ROOM

see that his/her nose was _____. He/She also complained
                             VERB ENDING IN "ING"

of _____-aches and having a sore _____, and I took
    PART OF THE BODY   NOUN

him/her to the family _____. The doctor quickly diagnosed
                          NOUN

it to be the _____-hour flu and suggested he/she take two
                NUMBER

_____ with a glass of _____ and go to bed _____.
 PLURAL NOUN   TYPE OF LIQUID   ADVERB

Dear Science Teacher,

Please excuse _____ for being late for your
                 ANOTHER PERSON IN ROOM

_____ science class. It's my fault. I feel _____.
 ADJECTIVE   ADJECTIVE

_____ was up until the _____ hours of the
 SAME PERSON IN ROOM   ADJECTIVE

morning completing his/her _____ project. Just as he/she was
                              ADJECTIVE

going out the _____ door, I noticed that his/her only pair of
                 ADJECTIVE

_____ had a/an _____ in them. It took me an hour to
 PLURAL NOUN   NOUN

find my _____ so I could see to _____ the needle,
          PLURAL NOUN   VERB

enabling me to sew his/her _____ back together.
                              PLURAL NOUN

From UPSIDE-DOWN MAD LIBS® • Copyright © 1995 by Price Stern Sloan,
an imprint of Penguin Group (USA) Inc., 345 Hudson Street, New York, NY 10014.

MAD LIBS® is fun to play with friends, but you can also play it by yourself! To begin with, DO NOT look at the story on the page below. Fill in the blanks on this page with the words called for. Then, using the words you have selected, fill in the blank spaces in the story.

Now you've created your own hilarious MAD LIBS® game!

SPEAKING OF SPEAKING

_____ ADJECTIVE

_____ VERB ENDING IN "ING"

_____ PLURAL NOUN

_____ NOUN

_____ PLURAL NOUN

_____ ADJECTIVE

_____ PLURAL NOUN

_____ PLURAL NOUN

_____ NOUN

_____ NOUN

_____ PART OF THE BODY

_____ ADJECTIVE

_____ ADJECTIVE

_____ PART OF THE BODY

_____ TYPE OF LIQUID

_____ PART OF THE BODY

MAD LIBS®
SPEAKING OF SPEAKING

A recent _____ poll shows that the majority of people are
　　　　　　ADJECTIVE

terrified of public _____. They would rather walk
　　　　　　　　VERB ENDING IN "ING"

across burning _____ or swim in _____-infested
　　　　　　PLURAL NOUN　　　　　　　　NOUN

waters than give a speech in front of a group of _____. This
　　　　　　　　　　　　　　　　　　　　　PLURAL NOUN

_____ fear can be overcome in five easy _____:
　ADJECTIVE　　　　　　　　　　　　　　　PLURAL NOUN

1. Organize all of your _____ on a piece of _____.
　　　　　　　　　　　PLURAL NOUN　　　　　　　　NOUN

2. Remember to start your speech with a funny _____.
　　　　　　　　　　　　　　　　　　　　　NOUN

3. When speaking, look your audience straight in the _____
　　　　　　　　　　　　　　　　　　　　　PART OF THE BODY

   and speak in a strong and _____ voice.
　　　　　　　　　　　　ADJECTIVE

4. Be simple. Never use _____ words that are over the
　　　　　　　　　　　ADJECTIVE

   audience's _____.
　　　　　PART OF THE BODY

5. Always keep a pitcher of _____ next to you, in case your
　　　　　　　　　　　TYPE OF LIQUID

   _____ goes dry.
　　PART OF THE BODY

From UPSIDE-DOWN MAD LIBS® • Copyright © 1995 by Price Stern Sloan,
an imprint of Penguin Group (USA) Inc., 345 Hudson Street, New York, NY 10014.

MAD LIBS® is fun to play with friends, but you can also play it by yourself! To begin with, DO NOT look at the story on the page below. Fill in the blanks on this page with the words called for. Then, using the words you have selected, fill in the blank spaces in the story.

Now you've created your own hilarious MAD LIBS® game!

VIDEO GAMES

VERB_____

NOUN_____

NOUN_____

VERB ENDING IN "ING"_____

NOUN_____

ADJECTIVE_____

PART OF THE BODY_____

PLURAL NOUN_____

ADJECTIVE_____

PART OF THE BODY_____

PLURAL NOUN_____

ADJECTIVE_____

PLURAL NOUN_____

ADJECTIVE_____

NUMBER_____

NOUN_____

PLURAL NOUN_____

MAD LIBS®
VIDEO GAMES

I love to _____ video games. I can play them day and
            VERB

_____! My mom and _____ are not too happy with my
   NOUN   NOUN

_____ so much time in front of the television _____.
VERB ENDING IN "ING"   NOUN

Although Dad believes that these _____ games help children
                                      ADJECTIVE

develop hand-_____ coordination and improve their
              PART OF THE BODY

learning _____, he also seems to think they have _____
          PLURAL NOUN   ADJECTIVE

side effects on one's _____. Both of my _____
                       PART OF THE BODY   PLURAL NOUN

think this is due to a/an _____ use of violence in the majority
                            ADJECTIVE

of the _____. Finally, we all arrived at a/an _____
         PLURAL NOUN   ADJECTIVE

compromise: After dinner I can play _____ hours of video games,
                                     NUMBER

provided I help clear the _____ and wash the _____.
                             NOUN   PLURAL NOUN

MAD LIBS® is fun to play with friends, but you can also play it by yourself! To begin with, DO NOT look at the story on the page below. Fill in the blanks on this page with the words called for. Then, using the words you have selected, fill in the blank spaces in the story.

Now you've created your own hilarious MAD LIBS® game!

AN ART NAMED MARTIAL

PLURAL NOUN _____

ADJECTIVE _____

PERSON IN ROOM _____

ADJECTIVE _____

NOUN _____

ADJECTIVE _____

PLURAL NOUN _____

ANIMAL _____

VERB _____

NOUN _____

NOUN _____

PART OF THE BODY _____

NOUN _____

NOUN _____

PART OF THE BODY (PLURAL) _____

MAD LIBS®
AN ART NAMED MARTIAL

Want to become an expert in Karate or Kung Fu? You can learn

martial _____ in three _____ lessons with Master
      PLURAL NOUN   ADJECTIVE

_____'s video tape. This _____-selling tape
    PERSON IN ROOM   ADJECTIVE

takes you step-by-_____ through a series of _____
             NOUN   ADJECTIVE

exercises guaranteed to develop _____ in your body and
                         PLURAL NOUN

make you strong as a/an _____. In less than a week, you will
               ANIMAL

be able to do one hundred _____-ups a day, skip a jumping
                    VERB

_____ for an hour, and climb a/an _____ without losing your
  NOUN   NOUN

_____. And believe it or not, by the end of the month,
  PART OF THE BODY

you'll not only be eligible for a black _____, but be capable
                        NOUN

of breaking a four-inch-thick _____ easily with your own
                    NOUN

two _____!
   PART OF THE BODY (PLURAL)

MAD LIBS® is fun to play with friends, but you can also play it by yourself! To begin with, DO NOT look at the story on the page below. Fill in the blanks on this page with the words called for. Then, using the words you have selected, fill in the blank spaces in the story.

Now you've created your own hilarious MAD LIBS® game!

THE FARM

ADJECTIVE _____

NOUN _____

PLURAL NOUN _____

VERB _____

NOUN _____

ADJECTIVE _____

PLURAL NOUN _____

VERB _____

PLURAL NOUN _____

NOUN _____

NOUN _____

VERB _____

MAD LIBS
THE FARM

I spent last summer on my grandfather's _____ farm. He
                                              ADJECTIVE

raises oats, wheat, and _____. Grandfather also grows lettuce,
                            NOUN

corn, and lima _____. My favorite place to _____ on
                  PLURAL NOUN   VERB

the farm is the _____ house where Grandfather keeps his
                     NOUN

_____ chickens. Every day, each hen lays round, smooth
      ADJECTIVE

_____. Grandfather sells most of them, but keeps some so
   PLURAL NOUN

the hens can _____ on them and hatch cute, fuzzy little
                   VERB

_____. I'm looking forward to next year, when Grandfather
   PLURAL NOUN

is going to show me how to drive his _____, sow the
                                              NOUN

_____, and _____ the cow.
    NOUN   VERB

MAD LIBS® is fun to play with friends, but you can also play it by yourself! To begin with, DO NOT look at the story on the page below. Fill in the blanks on this page with the words called for. Then, using the words you have selected, fill in the blank spaces in the story.

Now you've created your own hilarious MAD LIBS® game!

VCR REMOTE CONTROL, WHERE ART THOU?

PLURAL NOUN _____

NOUN _____

NOUN _____

NOUN _____

PLURAL NOUN _____

PLURAL NOUN _____

PART OF BODY (PLURAL) _____

NOUN _____

NOUN _____

NOUN _____

NOUN _____

ADJECTIVE _____

ADJECTIVE _____

MAD LIBS®
VCR REMOTE CONTROL, WHERE ART THOU?

A recent nationwide survey of over one hundred thousand _____
                                                        PLURAL NOUN

shows that the three articles most often misplaced are a woman's

hand _____, keys to the _____, and most of all, the
        NOUN   NOUN

videocassette recorder _____. The first place to look for your
                          NOUN

missing remote is the couch. Check behind the _____, in
                                                PLURAL NOUN

between the _____, and if necessary, get down on your hands
              PLURAL NOUN

and _____ and look under the _____ or coffee
      PART OF THE BODY (PLURAL)   NOUN

_____. Believe it or not, remotes have been found in such odd
   NOUN

places as the inside of a/an _____, under a pile of magazines,
                                NOUN

or floating in the bathroom _____. If you can't find your
                              NOUN

_____ remote, don't feel too bad . . . at least you don't have to
 ADJECTIVE

try to figure out how the _____ thing works!
                           ADJECTIVE

MAD LIBS® is fun to play with friends, but you can also play it by yourself! To begin with, DO NOT look at the story on the page below. Fill in the blanks on this page with the words called for. Then, using the words you have selected, fill in the blank spaces in the story.

Now you've created your own hilarious MAD LIBS® game!

SHOW-AND-TELL

_____ NOUN

_____ VERB ENDING IN "ING"

_____ ADVERB

_____ SOMETHING ALIVE

_____ NOUN

_____ ADJECTIVE

_____ VERB

_____ PERSON IN ROOM

_____ ADJECTIVE

_____ NOUN

_____ SOMETHING TO EAT

_____ VERB ENDING IN "ING"

_____ PLURAL NOUN

_____ NOUN

_____ NUMBER

MAD☺LIBS®
SHOW-AND-TELL

Today, I would like to show the class a/an _____ I caught when
<small>NOUN</small>

I went _____ with my aunt. I had never fished before,
<small>VERB ENDING IN "ING"</small>

but my aunt _____ taught me how to bait a hook with a/an
<small>ADVERB</small>

_____ and then how to cast the _____ into the
<small>SOMETHING ALIVE</small> <small>NOUN</small>

_____ lake. I _____ fishing!
<small>ADJECTIVE</small> <small>VERB</small>

My name is _____, and I would like to show the
<small>PERSON IN ROOM</small>

class this _____ _____ from my mother's kitchen.
<small>ADJECTIVE</small> <small>NOUN</small>

My mother uses it every morning to fix my _____. It is
<small>SOMETHING TO EAT</small>

also useful if you are into _____ or if you want to slice
<small>VERB ENDING IN "ING"</small>

up some _____. If you want one, you can buy it at your
<small>PLURAL NOUN</small>

local _____ store for only _____ dollars.
<small>NOUN</small> <small>NUMBER</small>

MAD LIBS® is fun to play with friends, but you can also play it by yourself! To begin with, DO NOT look at the story on the page below. Fill in the blanks on this page with the words called for. Then, using the words you have selected, fill in the blank spaces in the story.

Now you've created your own hilarious MAD LIBS® game!

GOOD TO THE LAST BYTE

_____ ANIMAL

_____ ADJECTIVE

_____ ADJECTIVE

_____ NOUN

_____ PLURAL NOUN

_____ VERB

_____ PLURAL NOUN

_____ VERB

_____ ADJECTIVE

_____ PART OF THE BODY

_____ PART OF THE BODY

_____ NOUN

_____ NOUN

MAD LIBS®
GOOD TO THE LAST BYTE

To be able to use a computer, you must have a keyboard, a monitor, and a handheld tracking device called a/an _____. In
ANIMAL

order to operate your _____ computer, a/an _____
ADJECTIVE   _ADJECTIVE_

disk or a floppy _____ are essential. Computers are very
NOUN

helpful for students because they store a million _____
PLURAL NOUN

of information in their hard _____ and correct misspelled
VERB

_____. They can also add, subtract, and _____ numbers.
PLURAL NOUN   _VERB_

Now, computers come in every shape and size, big and _____.
ADJECTIVE

The laptop computer, which sits on your _____, is small
PART OF THE BODY

enough that you can tuck it under your _____ or carry
PART OF THE BODY

it to school in your _____ bag. Today, the computer is as much
NOUN

a part of a household as the kitchen _____.
NOUN

MAD LIBS® is fun to play with friends, but you can also play it by yourself! To begin with, DO NOT look at the story on the page below. Fill in the blanks on this page with the words called for. Then, using the words you have selected, fill in the blank spaces in the story.

Now you've created your own hilarious MAD LIBS® game!

UPSIDE-DOWN DICTIONARY STARTING WITH LETTER *B*

ADJECTIVE_____

NOUN_____

NOUN_____

NOUN_____

ADJECTIVE_____

PLURAL NOUN_____

ADVERB_____

NOUN_____

VERB (PAST TENSE)_____

NOUN_____

PLURAL NOUN_____

ADVERB_____

NOUN_____

BALLOON (noun): A/An _____ bag that rises in the
ADJECTIVE

_____ when it is filled with hot _____
NOUN   NOUN

BAGEL (noun): A glazed _____-shaped roll with a/an
NOUN

_____ texture, made from _____ that are dropped
ADJECTIVE   PLURAL NOUN

into _____ boiling _____ and then baked
ADVERB   NOUN

BASEBALL (noun): A game _____ with a bat and a/an
VERB (PAST TENSE)

_____ by two teams of nine _____ each. These
NOUN   PLURAL NOUN

two teams play _____ in the _____ and at bat
ADVERB   NOUN

MAD LIBS® is fun to play with friends, but you can also play it by yourself! To begin with, DO NOT look at the story on the page below. Fill in the blanks on this page with the words called for. Then, using the words you have selected, fill in the blank spaces in the story.

Now you've created your own hilarious MAD LIBS® game!

THE PROM

_____
PART OF THE BODY

_____
PART OF THE BODY

_____
ADJECTIVE

_____
NOUN

_____
NOUN

_____
VERB (PAST TENSE)

_____
PLURAL NOUN

_____
NOUN

_____
NOUN

_____
PLURAL NOUN

_____
ADJECTIVE

_____
VERB ENDING IN "ING"

_____
ADJECTIVE

_____
NOUN

_____
NOUN

_____
NOUN

MAD LIBS®
THE PROM

If there's a melody you can't seem to get out of your _____

PART OF THE BODY

or a song running through your _____, then bring your

PART OF THE BODY

feet to this year's _____ prom. As usual, our _____

ADJECTIVE · NOUN

will be held in our high school _____. A dress code will be

NOUN

observed. No one will be admitted wearing _____ or

VERB (PAST TENSE)

torn _____. Girls must wear a/an _____ and

PLURAL NOUN · NOUN

boys must wear a dress shirt and a/an _____. As always, hot

NOUN

_____ will be served, and there will be _____

PLURAL NOUN · ADJECTIVE

prizes and an award for the best-_____ couple. The

VERB ENDING IN "ING"

_____ dance committee is also proud to announce that

ADJECTIVE

every girl who attends will receive a/an _____ to pin to her

NOUN

_____, and every boy will receive a complimentary _____.

NOUN · NOUN

From UPSIDE-DOWN MAD LIBS® · Copyright © 1995 by Price Stern Sloan,
an imprint of Penguin Group (USA) Inc., 345 Hudson Street, New York, NY 10014.

MAD LIBS® is fun to play with friends, but you can also play it by yourself! To begin with, DO NOT look at the story on the page below. Fill in the blanks on this page with the words called for. Then, using the words you have selected, fill in the blank spaces in the story.

Now you've created your own hilarious MAD LIBS® game!

TO WHOM IT MAY CONCERN

PERSON IN ROOM _____

NUMBER _____

ADVERB _____

NOUN _____

ADJECTIVE _____

VERB _____

ADJECTIVE _____

PLURAL NOUN _____

SAME PERSON IN ROOM _____

NOUN _____

PLURAL NOUN _____

NUMBER _____

SAME PERSON IN ROOM _____

ADJECTIVE _____

NOUN _____

VERB _____

MAD LIBS®
TO WHOM IT MAY CONCERN

I have known _____ for _____ years and _____
        PERSON IN ROOM   NUMBER   ADVERB

recommend him/her for the position of assistant _____ in your
                             NOUN

_____ company. I can't _____ enough about this person's
ADJECTIVE   VERB

_____ character and ability to get along with his/her fellow
ADJECTIVE

_____. As for educational background, _____
PLURAL NOUN   SAME PERSON IN ROOM

is a college _____, is capable of speaking several foreign
            NOUN

_____, and has an IQ of _____. You will find
PLURAL NOUN   NUMBER

_____ to be a/an _____ worker who is not only
SAME PERSON IN ROOM   ADJECTIVE

as smart as a/an _____, but who doesn't know the meaning of
         NOUN

the word _____. Unfortunately, this is one of many words
      VERB

this person doesn't know the meaning of.

MAD LIBS® is fun to play with friends, but you can also play it by yourself! To begin with, DO NOT look at the story on the page below. Fill in the blanks on this page with the words called for. Then, using the words you have selected, fill in the blank spaces in the story.

Now you've created your own hilarious MAD LIBS® game!

COMPUTERSPEAK

_____ NOUN

_____ PLURAL NOUN

_____ VERB

_____ NOUN

_____ WORD BEGINNING WITH "M"

_____ PLURAL NOUN

_____ PLURAL NOUN

_____ NOUN

_____ VERB

_____ PLURAL NOUN

_____ NOUN

_____ ADVERB

_____ NOUN

_____ ADJECTIVE

_____ PLURAL NOUN

_____ NOUN

MAD LIBS®
COMPUTERSPEAK

If you want to become _____ literate, here are some key
NOUN

_____ that you should _____ as quickly as possible:
PLURAL NOUN   VERB

CD-ROM: Stands for compact _____ . . . read only
                                        NOUN

_____ . This compact disc can hold as many as 600
WORD BEGINNING WITH "M"

_____ , which is the equivalent of 700 floppy _____ .
PLURAL NOUN   PLURAL NOUN

CYBERSPACE: Stands for the imaginary _____ that people
                                              NOUN

enter when they _____ with each other through computers on
                    VERB

a collection of _____ , known as the Inter- _____ .
                  PLURAL NOUN   NOUN

E-MAIL: Means _____ transmitted _____ .
                      ADVERB   NOUN

MODEM: Is the device that allows a/an _____ computer to
                                              ADJECTIVE

transmit _____ over a phone _____ .
            PLURAL NOUN   NOUN

MAD LIBS® is fun to play with friends, but you can also play it by yourself! To begin with, DO NOT look at the story on the page below. Fill in the blanks on this page with the words called for. Then, using the words you have selected, fill in the blank spaces in the story.

Now you've created your own hilarious MAD LIBS® game!

MORE GREAT EXCUSES
FOR TARDINESS

ADJECTIVE _____

PERSON IN ROOM (FIRST NAME) _____

ADJECTIVE _____

ANIMAL _____

ADJECTIVE _____

NUMBER _____

PART OF THE BODY (PLURAL) _____

ANOTHER PERSON (FIRST NAME) _____

PLURAL NOUN _____

NOUN _____

NOUN _____

ADJECTIVE _____

VERB (PAST TENSE) _____

NOUN _____

NOUN _____

ADJECTIVE _____

MAD LIBS®
MORE GREAT EXCUSES
FOR TARDINESS

Dear Principal,

I am sorry to have to tell you that my _____ son/daughter,
                                           ADJECTIVE

_____ will be unable to attend your _____
PERSON IN ROOM (FIRST NAME)   ADJECTIVE

school this week as he/she has caught a case of the _____ pox.
                                                     ANIMAL

The _____ doctor says that it will be _____ weeks before
     ADJECTIVE   NUMBER

he/she is healthy and back on his/her _____ again.
                                       PART OF THE BODY (PLURAL)

Dear Math Teacher,

I was driving _____ to school when the
              ANOTHER PERSON (FIRST NAME)

_____ failed and my car crashed into a/an _____. By
PLURAL NOUN   NOUN

the time the tow _____ finally arrived and the _____
                  NOUN   ADJECTIVE

mechanic _____ the _____ and recharged the
         VERB (PAST TENSE)   NOUN

_____, we had missed your _____ class.
NOUN   ADJECTIVE

MAD LIBS® is fun to play with friends, but you can also play it by yourself! To begin with, DO NOT look at the story on the page below. Fill in the blanks on this page with the words called for. Then, using the words you have selected, fill in the blank spaces in the story.

Now you've created your own hilarious MAD LIBS® game!

BICYCLE RIDING

_____ VERB ENDING IN "ING"

_____ ADJECTIVE

_____ PLURAL NOUN

_____ PART OF THE BODY

_____ ADVERB

_____ PART OF THE BODY

_____ ADJECTIVE

_____ NOUN

_____ PLURAL NOUN

_____ VERB

_____ PLURAL NOUN

_____ NOUN

_____ NOUN

_____ PART OF THE BODY

_____ VERB

MAD LIBS®
BICYCLE RIDING

Most doctors agree that bicycle _____ is a/an
                                    VERB ENDING IN "ING"

_____ form of exercise that benefits _____ of all ages.
ADJECTIVE   PLURAL NOUN

Riding a bicycle enables you to develop your _____
                                             PART OF THE BODY

muscles as well as _____ increase the rate of your _____
                   ADVERB   PART OF THE BODY

beat. Bicycle riding as also a/an _____ means of _____.
                                   ADJECTIVE   NOUN

More _____ around the world _____ bicycles than
     PLURAL NOUN   VERB

drive _____ . No matter what kind of _____ you ride,
      PLURAL NOUN   NOUN

always be sure to wear a/an _____ on your head and have
                            NOUN

reflectors on your _____ , especially if you _____ at night.
                   PART OF THE BODY   VERB

SOOPER DOOPER
MAD LIBS

by Roger Price & Leonard Stern

PSS!
PRICE STERN SLOAN
An Imprint of Penguin Group (USA) Inc.

PRICE STERN SLOAN

Penguin Group (USA) Inc., 375 Hudson Street, New York, New York 10014, USA
Penguin Group (Canada), 90 Eglinton Avenue East, Suite 700,
Toronto, Ontario M4P 2Y3, Canada (a division of Pearson Penguin Canada Inc.)
Penguin Books Ltd, 80 Strand, London WC2R 0RL, England
Penguin Ireland, 25 St Stephen's Green, Dublin 2, Ireland
(a division of Penguin Books Ltd)
Penguin Group (Australia), 707 Collins Street, Melbourne, Victoria 3008, Australia
(a division of Pearson Australia Group Pty Ltd)
Penguin Books India Pvt Ltd, 11 Community Centre,
Panchsheel Park, New Delhi—110 017, India
Penguin Group (NZ), 67 Apollo Drive, Rosedale, Auckland 0632, New Zealand
(a division of Pearson New Zealand Ltd)
Penguin Books, Rosebank Office Park, 181 Jan Smuts Avenue,
Parktown North 2193, South Africa
Penguin China, B7 Jiaming Center, 27 East Third Ring Road North,
Chaoyang District, Beijing 100020, China

Penguin Books Ltd, Registered Offices:
80 Strand, London WC2R 0RL, England

Published by Price Stern Sloan, a division of Penguin Young Readers Group,
345 Hudson Street, New York, New York 10014.
Printed in the United States of America. Published simultaneously in Canada.

ISBN 0-8431-0057-5

MAD LIBS

INSTRUCTIONS

MAD LIBS® is a game for people who don't like games!
It can be played by one, two, three, four, or forty.

• RIDICULOUSLY SIMPLE DIRECTIONS

In this tablet you will find stories containing blank spaces where words are left out. One player, the READER, selects one of these stories. The READER does not tell anyone what the story is about. Instead, he/she asks the other players, the WRITERS, to give him/her words. These words are used to fill in the blank spaces in the story.

• TO PLAY

The READER asks each WRITER in turn to call out a word—an adjective or a noun or whatever the space calls for—and uses them to fill in the blank spaces in the story. The result is a MAD LIBS® game.

When the READER then reads the completed MAD LIBS® game to the other players, they will discover that they have written a story that is fantastic, screamingly funny, shocking, silly, crazy, or just plain dumb—depending upon which words each WRITER called out.

• EXAMPLE (*Before* and *After*)

" _____ !" he said _____
    EXCLAMATION   ADVERB

as he jumped into his convertible _____ and
                                 NOUN

drove off with his _____ wife.
                ADJECTIVE

" *Ouch* !" he said *stupidly*
    EXCLAMATION   ADVERB

as he jumped into his convertible *cat* and
                                 NOUN

drove off with his *brave* wife.
                ADJECTIVE

In case you have forgotten what adjectives, adverbs, nouns, and verbs are, here is a quick review:

An ADJECTIVE describes something or somebody. *Lumpy*, *soft*, *ugly*, *messy*, and *short* are adjectives.

An ADVERB tells how something is done. It modifies a verb and usually ends in "ly." *Modestly*, *stupidly*, *greedily*, and *carefully* are adverbs.

A NOUN is the name of a person, place, or thing. *Sidewalk*, *umbrella*, *bridle*, *bathtub*, and *nose* are nouns.

A VERB is an action word. *Run*, *pitch*, *jump*, and *swim* are verbs. Put the verbs in past tense if the directions say PAST TENSE. *Ran*, *pitched*, *jumped*, and *swam* are verbs in the past tense.

When we ask for A PLACE, we mean any sort of place: a country or city (*Spain*, *Cleveland*) or a room (*bathroom*, *kitchen*).

An EXCLAMATION or SILLY WORD is any sort of funny sound, gasp, grunt, or outcry, like *Wow!*, *Ouch!*, *Whomp!*, *Ick!*, and *Gadzooks!*

When we ask for specific words, like a NUMBER, a COLOR, an ANIMAL, or a PART OF THE BODY, we mean a word that is one of those things, like *seven*, *blue*, *horse*, or *head*.

When we ask for a PLURAL, it means more than one. For example, *cat* pluralized is *cats*.

MAD LIBS® is fun to play with friends, but you can also play it by yourself! To begin with, DO NOT look at the story on the page below. Fill in the blanks on this page with the words called for. Then, using the words you have selected, fill in the blank spaces in the story.

Now you've created your own hilarious MAD LIBS® game!

FATHER GOOSE RHYMES

_____ NOUN

_____ ADJECTIVE

_____ ANIMAL

_____ SAME NOUN

_____ ADJECTIVE

_____ ADJECTIVE

_____ NOUN

_____ TYPE OF CONTAINER

_____ NOUN

_____ PART OF THE BODY

_____ ADJECTIVE

_____ ADJECTIVE

_____ ADJECTIVE

_____ ADJECTIVE

_____ VERB (PAST TENSE)

_____ PLURAL NOUN

MAD LIBS

FATHER GOOSE RHYMES

Old Mother Hubbard went to the _____
NOUN

To get her _____ _____ a bone.
ADJECTIVE ANIMAL

When she got there, the _____ was _____,
SAME NOUN ADJECTIVE

And so her _____ dog had none.
ADJECTIVE

    Jack and Jill went up the _____
NOUN

    To fetch a/an _____ of water.
TYPE OF CONTAINER

    Jack fell down and broke his _____,
NOUN

    And Jill came tumbling after.

There was a little girl, and she had a little curl

Right in the middle of her _____.
PART OF THE BODY

And when she was _____, she was very, very _____,
ADJECTIVE ADJECTIVE

And when she was bad, she was _____.
ADJECTIVE

    There was a/an _____ woman
ADJECTIVE

Who _____ in a shoe.
VERB (PAST TENSE)

She had so many _____,
PLURAL NOUN

She didn't know what to do.

MORE
FATHER GOOSE RHYMES

_____ NOUN

_____ ANIMAL

_____ NOUN THAT RHYMES WITH "MOON"

_____ NOUN THAT RHYMES WITH "MOON"

_____ NOUN

_____ NOUN THAT RHYMES WITH "DAY"

_____ ANIMAL

_____ MUSICAL INSTRUMENT

_____ PLACE

_____ TYPE OF VEGETABLE

_____ ADJECTIVE

_____ NOUN

_____ ANIMAL

_____ NOUN

_____ SAME ANIMAL

_____ VERB THAT RHYMES WITH "SNOW"

MAD LIBS
MORE FATHER
GOOSE RHYMES

Hi, diddle, diddle, the _____ and the fiddle,
                          NOUN

The _____ jumped over the _____.
        ANIMAL   NOUN THAT RHYMES WITH "MOON"

The little dog laughed to see such sport,

And the dish ran away with the _____.
                                 NOUN THAT RHYMES WITH "MOON"

Little Miss Muffet sat on a/an _____,
                                      NOUN

Eating her curds and _____.
                       NOUN THAT RHYMES WITH "DAY"

Along came a/an _____ and sat down beside her
                    ANIMAL

And frightened Miss Muffet away.

Little Boy Blue, come blow your _____.
                                  MUSICAL INSTRUMENT

The sheep's in the _____, the cow's in the _____.
                        PLACE   TYPE OF VEGETABLE

Where is the _____ boy who looks after the sheep?
                 ADJECTIVE

He's under the _____, fast asleep.
                     NOUN

Mary had a little _____.
                        ANIMAL

Its _____ was white as snow.
         NOUN

And everywhere that Mary went

Her _____ was sure to _____.
        SAME ANIMAL   VERB THAT RHYMES WITH "SNOW"

MAD LIBS® is fun to play with friends, but you can also play it by yourself! To begin with, DO NOT look at the story on the page below. Fill in the blanks on this page with the words called for. Then, using the words you have selected, fill in the blank spaces in the story.

Now you've created your own hilarious MAD LIBS® game!

BIRD WATCHING AND VICE VERSA

PLURAL NOUN _____

ADJECTIVE _____

ADJECTIVE _____

NOUN _____

FUNNY NOISE _____

VERB _____

NUMBER _____

ADJECTIVE _____

ADJECTIVE _____

PART OF THE BODY _____

PLURAL NOUN _____

NOUN _____

ADJECTIVE _____

NOUN _____

MAD LIBS®
BIRD WATCHING AND VICE VERSA

Bird watching can be more fun than a barrel of _____ .
PLURAL NOUN

Our _____ feathered friends are everywhere, waiting to be
ADJECTIVE

watched. An interesting bird to start with is the _____
ADJECTIVE

oriole, which builds its nest in _____ trees. Early in
NOUN

spring, we hear the oriole give its mating call, which sounds like this:

" _____ ." Then the male and female get together and
FUNNY NOISE

_____ . Later, the female lays _____ eggs. Isn't
VERB   NUMBER

that _____ ? Another fascinating bird is the
ADJECTIVE

_____ -breasted nuthatch. The nuthatch is very tame.
ADJECTIVE

He will fly down and land right on your _____
PART OF THE BODY

and eat out of your _____ . Other birds to
PLURAL NOUN

watch out for are the red-crested _____ , the
NOUN

_____ -necked thrush, and the yellow-bellied
ADJECTIVE

_____ sucker. Now that you know something about
NOUN

birds, get out there and watch!

MAD LIBS® is fun to play with friends, but you can also play it by yourself! To begin with, DO NOT look at the story on the page below. Fill in the blanks on this page with the words called for. Then, using the words you have selected, fill in the blank spaces in the story.

Now you've created your own hilarious MAD LIBS® game!

A BASEBALL BROADCAST

COLOR _____

PLURAL NOUN _____

ADJECTIVE _____

CELEBRITY _____

ADJECTIVE _____

NOUN _____

NUMBER _____

NUMBER _____

NOUN _____

ADJECTIVE _____

ANOTHER CELEBRITY _____

ANOTHER CELEBRITY _____

ADJECTIVE _____

NOUN _____

ANOTHER CELEBRITY _____

ADJECTIVE _____

MAD LIBS
A BASEBALL BROADCAST

Ladies and gentlemen, this is _____ Barber, your sportscaster,
                                    COLOR

bringing you the last inning of the game between the Cleveland

_____ and the _____ Yankees. _____ is
  PLURAL NOUN   ADJECTIVE   CELEBRITY

pitching for the Yankees. Here's the pitch! It's a low _____
                                                          ADJECTIVE

ball that just cuts the inside of the _____ for a strike. That
                                           NOUN

makes the count _____ strikes and _____ balls. Now
                     NUMBER   NUMBER

here's the next pitch. The batter swings and connects. It's a long, high

_____ out to _____ field. But _____
    NOUN   ADJECTIVE   ANOTHER CELEBRITY

is coming up fast and has it for the second out. The next batter up

is _____ , the Cleveland _____ -stop. Here's
    ANOTHER CELEBRITY   ADJECTIVE

the pitch . . . and it's hit . . . a short ground ball to third _____ .
                                                                    NOUN

_____ scoops it up and throws it to first base for an out,
ANOTHER CELEBRITY

and the game is over. And the Yankees move into second place in the

_____ League!
  ADJECTIVE

MAD LIBS® is fun to play with friends, but you can also play it by yourself! To begin with, DO NOT look at the story on the page below. Fill in the blanks on this page with the words called for. Then, using the words you have selected, fill in the blank spaces in the story.

Now you've created your own hilarious MAD LIBS® game!

MOTHER AND SON

ADJECTIVE _____

NOUN _____

PLURAL NOUN _____

PLURAL NOUN _____

ADJECTIVE _____

NOUN _____

DAY OF THE WEEK _____

PART OF THE BODY (PLURAL) _____

EXCLAMATION _____

NOUN _____

ADJECTIVE _____

NOUN _____

MAD LIBS
MOTHER AND SON

MOTHER: Junior, you come right inside. You're late, and your supper

is getting _____.
<u>ADJECTIVE</u>

SON: Aw, Mom. I've been out playing _____ ball with
<u>NOUN</u>

some of the other _____.
<u>PLURAL NOUN</u>

MOTHER: Well, get inside. And don't forget to wipe your muddy

_____.
<u>PLURAL NOUN</u>

SON: Okay, Mom. Can I watch television while I eat? There's

a/an _____ new show on.
<u>ADJECTIVE</u>

MOTHER: No, not while you're eating your _____.
<u>NOUN</u>

SON: But Mom! _____ Night Football is on.
<u>DAY OF THE WEEK</u>

MOTHER: No, sir. You've been watching too much television. You're

liable to strain your _____.
<u>PART OF THE BODY (PLURAL)</u>

SON: _____! That's my favorite program.
<u>EXCLAMATION</u>

MOTHER: Never mind. Go and wash your _____.
<u>NOUN</u>

SON: Aw, Mom. I don't have to. I'm _____.
<u>ADJECTIVE</u>

MOTHER: Don't talk back to me, young man, or I'll have to speak to

your _____.
<u>NOUN</u>

From SOOPER DOOPER MAD LIBS® • Copyright © 2001, 1988 by Price Stern Sloan,
an imprint of Penguin Group (USA) Inc., 345 Hudson Street, New York, NY 10014.

MAD LIBS® is fun to play with friends, but you can also play it by yourself! To begin with, DO NOT look at the story on the page below. Fill in the blanks on this page with the words called for. Then, using the words you have selected, fill in the blank spaces in the story.

Now you've created your own hilarious MAD LIBS® game!

WEATHER REPORT

GEOGRAPHIC LOCATION_____

ADJECTIVE_____

PLURAL NOUN_____

ADJECTIVE_____

PLURAL NOUN_____

NUMBER_____

NUMBER_____

ARTICLE OF CLOTHING_____

MAD LIBS®
WEATHER REPORT

Here is tomorrow's weather report for _____
GEOGRAPHIC LOCATION

and vicinity. Early tomorrow, a/an _____ front will
ADJECTIVE

collide with a mass of hot _____ moving from the
PLURAL NOUN

north. This means we can expect _____ winds and
ADJECTIVE

occasional _____ by late afternoon. Wind velocity will
PLURAL NOUN

be _____ miles an hour, and the high temperature should
NUMBER

be around _____ degrees. So if you're going out, you had
NUMBER

better plan on wearing your _____.
ARTICLE OF CLOTHING

MAD LIBS® is fun to play with friends, but you can also play it by yourself! To begin with, DO NOT look at the story on the page below. Fill in the blanks on this page with the words called for. Then, using the words you have selected, fill in the blank spaces in the story.

Now you've created your own hilarious MAD LIBS® game!

ITEMS FROM
A GOSSIP COLUMN

PERSON IN ROOM (FEMALE) _____

PERSON IN ROOM (MALE) _____

PLURAL NOUN _____

ANOTHER PERSON IN ROOM (MALE) _____

ANOTHER PERSON IN ROOM (FEMALE) _____

SAME PERSON (FEMALE) _____

ARTICLE OF CLOTHING _____

MAD LIBS®
ITEMS FROM
A GOSSIP COLUMN

_____ and her ex-husband, _____ ,
PERSON IN ROOM (FEMALE)   PERSON IN ROOM (MALE)

were seen last night at the Twenty-Three Club holding

_____ . Could it be reconciliation? The international heartthrob,
PLURAL NOUN

_____ , and the glamorous top model,
ANOTHER PERSON IN ROOM (MALE)

_____ , are expecting their first baby
ANOTHER PERSON IN ROOM (FEMALE)

in November. _____ is denying stork rumors,
SAME PERSON (FEMALE)

but yesterday she was seen buying a maternity _____ .
ARTICLE OF CLOTHING

MAD LIBS® is fun to play with friends, but you can also play it by yourself! To begin with, DO NOT look at the story on the page below. Fill in the blanks on this page with the words called for. Then, using the words you have selected, fill in the blank spaces in the story.

Now you've created your own hilarious MAD LIBS® game!

SUPERSTITIONS

ADVERB
_____

PLURAL NOUN
_____

ADJECTIVE
_____

PLURAL NOUN
_____

PART OF THE BODY
_____

ADJECTIVE
_____

ANIMAL
_____

ADJECTIVE
_____

NOUN
_____

NUMBER
_____

ADJECTIVE
_____

VERB
_____

PART OF THE BODY
_____

ADJECTIVE
_____

SOMETHING EDIBLE
_____

PART OF THE BODY
_____

MAD LIBS®
SUPERSTITIONS

Although we believe ourselves to be _____ civilized, most
ADVERB

of us are really _____ at heart, because we still believe in
PLURAL NOUN

_____ superstitions that began while humans still lived in
ADJECTIVE

_____. Some of these superstitions are:
PLURAL NOUN

1. If you spill salt, throw some over your left _____
PART OF THE BODY

    for _____ luck.
    ADJECTIVE

2. If a black _____ runs in front of you, you are in
    ANIMAL

    _____ trouble.
    ADJECTIVE

3. If you break a/an _____, you will have _____
    NOUN   NUMBER

    years of _____ luck.
    ADJECTIVE

4. Never _____ under a ladder.
    VERB

5. If your _____ itches, it means you will have a/an
    PART OF THE BODY

    _____ visitor.
    ADJECTIVE

6. If you want to keep vampires away from you, always wear

    _____ on a string around your _____.
    SOMETHING EDIBLE   PART OF THE BODY

From SOOPER DOOPER MAD LIBS® • Copyright © 2001, 1988 by Price Stern Sloan,
an imprint of Penguin Group (USA) Inc., 345 Hudson Street, New York, NY 10014.

MAD LIBS® is fun to play with friends, but you can also play it by yourself! To begin with, DO NOT look at the story on the page below. Fill in the blanks on this page with the words called for. Then, using the words you have selected, fill in the blank spaces in the story.

Now you've created your own hilarious MAD LIBS® game!

CHINESE DINNER

ADJECTIVE_____

ADJECTIVE_____

CELEBRITY_____

ADJECTIVE_____

NOUN_____

ADJECTIVE_____

ADJECTIVE_____

NOUN_____

NOUN_____

TYPE OF FOOD_____

ANOTHER TYPE OF FOOD_____

NOUN_____

ANOTHER TYPE OF FOOD_____

ADJECTIVE_____

MAD LIBS®
CHINESE DINNER

I recently had dinner at a new Chinese restaurant. The cooking was

_____ and the service was _____. The owner
ADJECTIVE   ADJECTIVE

of the restaurant, _____, suggested that for my first
CELEBRITY

course I have sweet and _____ spare ribs, which is a
ADJECTIVE

specialty of the _____. They were _____. For
NOUN   ADJECTIVE

the next course, I was served a/an _____ _____
ADJECTIVE   NOUN

soup. The main course consisted of Egg Foo _____,
NOUN

lobster in _____ sauce, and pressed _____.
TYPE OF FOOD   ANOTHER TYPE OF FOOD

For dessert, I ordered those famous Chinese _____ cookies
NOUN

with sliced _____. But whenever I eat Chinese food,
ANOTHER TYPE OF FOOD

an hour later I feel _____ again.
ADJECTIVE

HAMLET

CELEBRITY _____

ADJECTIVE _____

NOUN _____

TYPE OF LIQUID _____

NOUN _____

NOUN _____

PLURAL NOUN _____

PLURAL NOUN _____

PLURAL NOUN _____

PLURAL NOUN _____

VERB _____

VERB _____

VERB _____

NOUN _____

MAD☺LIBS®
HAMLET

This is the soliloquy from the play *Hamlet*, written by _____ .
_____ CELEBRITY

In the third act of this _____ play, Hamlet, who is sometimes
_____ ADJECTIVE

called "the melancholy _____ ," is suspicious of his stepfather
_____ NOUN

and hires some actors to act out a scene in which a king is killed

when someone pours _____ into his _____ . First,
_____ TYPE OF LIQUID _____ NOUN

however, he declaims: To be or not to be: that is the _____ :
_____ NOUN

Whether 'tis nobler in the mind to suffer the _____ and
_____ PLURAL NOUN

_____ of outrageous fortune, or to take arms against a sea of
PLURAL NOUN

_____ , and by opposing end them. To die: to sleep; no more;
PLURAL NOUN

and by a sleep to say we end the heartache and the thousand natural

_____ that flesh is heir to, 'tis a consummation devoutly to
PLURAL NOUN

be wish'd. To die, to _____ ; to _____ : perchance to
_____ VERB _____ VERB

_____ : ay, there's the _____ .
VERB _____ NOUN

MAD LIBS® is fun to play with friends, but you can also play it by yourself! To begin with, DO NOT look at the story on the page below. Fill in the blanks on this page with the words called for. Then, using the words you have selected, fill in the blank spaces in the story.

Now you've created your own hilarious MAD LIBS® game!

HAPPY BIRTHDAY!

PERSON IN ROOM (FEMALE) _____

NOUN _____

ADJECTIVE _____

NOUN _____

NUMBER _____

ADJECTIVE _____

PERSON IN ROOM (MALE) _____

NOUN _____

PART OF THE BODY _____

PLURAL NOUN _____

NOUN _____

ADJECTIVE _____

NOUN _____

NUMBER _____

ADJECTIVE _____

PLURAL NOUN _____

NOUN _____

MAD LIBS®
HAPPY BIRTHDAY!

Friends, this is a surprise party for _____.

PERSON IN ROOM (FEMALE)

We are here to celebrate her _____. All of her most

NOUN

_____ friends are here, including me, her devoted and

ADJECTIVE

faithful _____. I must say that she doesn't look a day over

NOUN

_____. Naturally, we have some _____ presents

NUMBER   ADJECTIVE

for her. _____ bought her a beautiful copper

PERSON IN ROOM (MALE)

_____ that she can wear on her lovely _____.

NOUN   PART OF THE BODY

And our hostess got her a dozen _____ that she can hang

PLURAL NOUN

in her _____. And we had the bakery send up a huge

NOUN

_____ _____ with _____ candles on it.

ADJECTIVE   NOUN   NUMBER

We all want to wish her a very _____ birthday and

ADJECTIVE

many happy _____. Now, let's all sing together: "Happy

PLURAL NOUN

_____-day to you!"

NOUN

(Editor's note: Sing until all are exhausted.)

MAD LIBS® is fun to play with friends, but you can also play it by yourself! To begin with, DO NOT look at the story on the page below. Fill in the blanks on this page with the words called for. Then, using the words you have selected, fill in the blank spaces in the story.

Now you've created your own hilarious MAD LIBS® game!

WAITER AND CUSTOMER

_____ NOUN

_____ NOUN

_____ TYPE OF FOOD

_____ NOUN

_____ ADJECTIVE

_____ NOUN

_____ ADJECTIVE

_____ ADJECTIVE

_____ PLURAL NOUN

_____ NOUN

_____ ADJECTIVE

_____ NOUN

_____ ADJECTIVE

_____ TYPE OF LIQUID

MAD LIBS®
WAITER AND CUSTOMER

SCENE: A restaurant—where else?

CUSTOMER: Oh, waiter! Would you please bring me a/an _____?
                          NOUN

I want to see what today's specials are.

WAITER: Today's specials are cream of _____ soup and
                                          NOUN

T-bone _____. Does that sound good?
        TYPE OF FOOD

CUSTOMER: Yes, but I'll have the roast prime _____ of
                                                  NOUN

beef with the _____ pudding.
              ADJECTIVE

WAITER: We're out of that. How about a sizzling sirloin _____
                                                            NOUN

and a/an _____ green salad?
          ADJECTIVE

CUSTOMER: No, thanks, I'd rather have the _____ fried chicken.
                                              ADJECTIVE

WAITER: Sorry, but we're out of that, too. How about soft-shell

_____?
PLURAL NOUN

CUSTOMER: No, thanks. Do you have any roast Long Island _____?
                                                            NOUN

WAITER: Sorry, no. Why don't you try our _____ goulash
                                              ADJECTIVE

with homemade _____ sauce?
              NOUN

CUSTOMER: No, thanks. Just bring me a/an _____ egg
                                             ADJECTIVE

sandwich and a cup of black _____.
                           TYPE OF LIQUID

MAD LIBS® is fun to play with friends, but you can also play it by yourself! To begin with, DO NOT look at the story on the page below. Fill in the blanks on this page with the words called for. Then, using the words you have selected, fill in the blank spaces in the story.

Now you've created your own hilarious MAD LIBS® game!

LETTER TO
A LOVELORN COLUMNIST

NUMBER _____

VERB ENDING IN "S" _____

VERB (PAST TENSE) _____

PLURAL NOUN _____

VERB _____

PLURAL NOUN _____

ADJECTIVE _____

PART OF THE BODY _____

ADJECTIVE _____

PERSON IN ROOM (FEMALE) _____

ADJECTIVE _____

VERB ENDING IN "ING" _____

VERB ENDING IN "ING" _____

PLURAL NOUN _____

VERB _____

SAME PLURAL NOUN _____

NUMBER _____

MAD LIBS
LETTER TO
A LOVELORN COLUMNIST

Dear Miss Lonelyhearts:

I've been engaged to the same man for _____ years. He keeps
                                        NUMBER

telling me he _____ me, but we need to wait to get
                VERB ENDING IN "S"

_____ until he makes more _____. If we
     VERB (PAST TENSE)   PLURAL NOUN

marry now, we will have to _____ with my mother and eat
                                VERB

_____ every day. But isn't _____ love worth
     PLURAL NOUN   ADJECTIVE

that? Should I put my _____ down and set a date, or just
                        PART OF THE BODY

continue to be _____?
                    ADJECTIVE

                            Signed,

                    _____
                        PERSON IN ROOM (FEMALE)

Dear Young Lady:

Don't do anything _____. Something worth
                            ADJECTIVE

_____ is worth _____ for. I don't think
VERB ENDING IN "ING"   VERB ENDING IN "ING"

eating _____ with the man you _____ is bad,
           PLURAL NOUN   VERB

but eating _____ and living _____ miles away from
            SAME PLURAL NOUN   NUMBER

your mother is better.

                    Signed,
                    Miss Lonelyhearts

MAD LIBS® is fun to play with friends, but you can also play it by yourself! To begin with, DO NOT look at the story on the page below. Fill in the blanks on this page with the words called for. Then, using the words you have selected, fill in the blank spaces in the story.

Now you've created your own hilarious MAD LIBS® game!

TOO MUCH FATHER GOOSE

ADJECTIVE_____

OCCUPATION_____

PLURAL NOUN_____

NOUN_____

SAME ADJECTIVE_____

ADJECTIVE_____

NOUN_____

ADJECTIVE_____

ADJECTIVE_____

ADJECTIVE_____

NOUN_____

ADJECTIVE_____

TYPE OF FOOD_____

PART OF THE BODY_____

NOUN_____

NOUN_____

ADJECTIVE_____

ADJECTIVE_____

NOUN_____

NOUN_____

PLURAL NOUN_____

MAD LIBS®
TOO MUCH FATHER GOOSE

Three _____ mice. See how they run!
     ADJECTIVE

They all ran after the farmer's _____,
                     OCCUPATION

Who cut off their _____ with a carving _____ .
            PLURAL NOUN   NOUN

Did you ever see such a sight in your life as three _____ mice?
                                     SAME ADJECTIVE

There was a crooked man, and he went a/an _____ mile.
                                  ADJECTIVE

He found a/an _____ against a/an _____ stile.
              NOUN   ADJECTIVE

He bought a/an _____ cat, which caught a/an _____ mouse,
             ADJECTIVE   ADJECTIVE

And they all lived together in a little crooked _____ .
                                    NOUN

_____ Jack Horner sat in the corner, eating his _____ pie.
  ADJECTIVE   TYPE OF FOOD

He stuck in his _____ and pulled out a/an _____ ,
            PART OF THE BODY   NOUN

And said, "What a good _____ am I!"
                    NOUN

Old King Cole was a/an _____ old soul,
                    ADJECTIVE

A/An _____ old soul was he.
     ADJECTIVE

He called for his _____ , and he called for his _____ ,
            NOUN   NOUN

And he called for his _____ three.
            PLURAL NOUN

MAD LIBS® is fun to play with friends, but you can also play it by yourself! To begin with, DO NOT look at the story on the page below. Fill in the blanks on this page with the words called for. Then, using the words you have selected, fill in the blank spaces in the story.

Now you've created your own hilarious MAD LIBS® game!

MEDICAL QUESTIONS AND ANSWERS

PERSON IN ROOM _____

ANOTHER PERSON IN ROOM _____

ADJECTIVE _____

NOUN _____

NOUN _____

NOUN _____

NOUN _____

ADJECTIVE _____

ADJECTIVE _____

ADJECTIVE _____

NOUN _____

TYPE OF LIQUID _____

PLURAL NOUN _____

NUMBER _____

PART OF THE BODY _____

NOUN _____

NOUN _____

MAD LIBS®
MEDICAL QUESTIONS
AND ANSWERS

The patient to be played by _____,
PERSON IN ROOM

the doctor to be played by _____.
ANOTHER PERSON IN ROOM

PATIENT: Doctor, whenever I stand up I get a/an _____ pain
ADJECTIVE

in my _____. Is this serious?
NOUN

DOCTOR: Sounds as if you have an inflammation of your _____.
NOUN

You need an anti-_____ shot.
NOUN

PATIENT: Doctor, I'm thinking of having my _____ removed.
NOUN

Is this a/an _____ operation?
ADJECTIVE

DOCTOR: No, the operation is quite _____, providing you
ADJECTIVE

have _____ kidneys.
ADJECTIVE

PATIENT: What are the symptoms of an overactive _____?
NOUN

DOCTOR: High _____ pressure. Also, severe _____
TYPE OF LIQUID   PLURAL NOUN

in the abdomen.

PATIENT: Doctor, is it possible for a/an _____-year-old man to
NUMBER

have a/an _____ attack?
PART OF THE BODY

DOCTOR: Only if he doesn't watch his _____ and eats too
NOUN

much _____.
NOUN

From SOOPER DOOPER MAD LIBS® • Copyright © 2001, 1988 by Price Stern Sloan,
an imprint of Penguin Group (USA) Inc., 345 Hudson Street, New York, NY 10014.

MAD LIBS® is fun to play with friends, but you can also play it by yourself! To begin with, DO NOT look at the story on the page below. Fill in the blanks on this page with the words called for. Then, using the words you have selected, fill in the blank spaces in the story.

Now you've created your own hilarious MAD LIBS® game!

COUNTRY AND WESTERN

ADJECTIVE
_____

ADJECTIVE
_____

ARTICLE OF CLOTHING (PLURAL)
_____

PLURAL NOUN
_____

ANIMAL (PLURAL)
_____

VERB ENDING IN "ING"
_____

PART OF THE BODY
_____

VERB
_____

ADJECTIVE
_____

PLURAL NOUN
_____

PLURAL NOUN
_____

MAD☺LIBS®
COUNTRY AND WESTERN

The most _____ music in the U.S. today is called
ADJECTIVE

"Country and _____" music. The musicians all wear
ADJECTIVE

cowboy _____ and play electric _____.
ARTICLE OF CLOTHING (PLURAL)   PLURAL NOUN

They sing about roping _____ and _____
ANIMAL (PLURAL)   VERB ENDING IN "ING"

out in the stable. In a lot of songs, the people end up with a broken

_____ and vow they will never _____ again.
PART OF THE BODY   VERB

Most country records are made in Nashville, Tennessee, the home of

the _____ Old Opry. Most cowboys are just ordinary
ADJECTIVE

_____ who wear big hats and tell even bigger _____.
PLURAL NOUN   PLURAL NOUN

From SOOPER DOOPER MAD LIBS® • Copyright © 2001, 1988 by Price Stern Sloan,
an imprint of Penguin Group (USA) Inc., 345 Hudson Street, New York, NY 10014.

MAD LIBS® is fun to play with friends, but you can also play it by yourself! To begin with, DO NOT look at the story on the page below. Fill in the blanks on this page with the words called for. Then, using the words you have selected, fill in the blank spaces in the story.

Now you've created your own hilarious MAD LIBS® game!

THE STOCK MARKET
(CAPITALISM MADE EASY)

_____ PLURAL NOUN

_____ ADJECTIVE

_____ SAME PLURAL NOUN

_____ ANIMAL

_____ NOUN

_____ ADJECTIVE

_____ ADJECTIVE

_____ PLURAL NOUN

_____ NOUN

_____ ADJECTIVE

_____ NOUN

_____ NOUN

_____ ADJECTIVE

_____ NOUN

_____ PLURAL NOUN

_____ ADJECTIVE

_____ NOUN

MAD LIBS
THE STOCK MARKET
(CAPITALISM MADE EASY)

This is how I made one million _____ in the stock market.
PLURAL NOUN

It's simple. At the present time, any _____ investor with a little
ADJECTIVE

capital should be able to double his _____ in a few months.
SAME PLURAL NOUN

All the experts agree that we are nearing the end of the _____
ANIMAL

market. Just recently, for instance, the American _____ and
NOUN

Foundry Company has shown a/an _____ trend. Conditions
ADJECTIVE

indicate a/an _____ market for their principal product,
ADJECTIVE

automatic _____. International Telephone and _____
PLURAL NOUN   NOUN

Company also looks _____. At the end of the last fiscal
ADJECTIVE

_____, they were earning $10 a/an _____. Another
NOUN   NOUN

_____ tip is Consolidated _____. This outfit
ADJECTIVE   NOUN

manufactures and sells electronic _____ of a very _____
PLURAL NOUN   ADJECTIVE

quality. But whatever you do, act now. Remember, prosperity is just

around the _____.
NOUN

MAD LIBS® is fun to play with friends, but you can also play it by yourself! To begin with, DO NOT look at the story on the page below. Fill in the blanks on this page with the words called for. Then, using the words you have selected, fill in the blank spaces in the story.

Now you've created your own hilarious MAD LIBS® game!

THE PLUMBER'S VISIT

PERSON IN ROOM (FEMALE)_____

PERSON IN ROOM (MALE)_____

ADVERB_____

NOUN_____

NOUN_____

ADJECTIVE_____

NOUN_____

TYPE OF LIQUID_____

NOUN_____

EXCLAMATION_____

ADJECTIVE_____

NOUN_____

NOUN_____

PLURAL NOUN_____

NOUN_____

VERB_____

MAD LIBS®
THE PLUMBER'S VISIT

A dramatic scene to be played by _____
PERSON IN ROOM (FEMALE)

and _____.
PERSON IN ROOM (MALE)

GIRL: Are you the plumber I sent for?

BOY: Yes, madam. I came over as _____ as I could.
ADVERB

Is there something wrong with your _____ ?
NOUN

GIRL: No, it's my _____ . The _____ thing is
NOUN   ADJECTIVE

all stopped up.

BOY: Have you tried cleaning it with a/an _____ ?
NOUN

GIRL: Yes, but there was too much _____ in the _____ .
TYPE OF LIQUID   NOUN

BOY: _____ ! This looks like it's going to be a/an
EXCLAMATION

_____ job!
ADJECTIVE

GIRL: Do you think I'll need a new _____ ?
NOUN

BOY: Only if your _____ is cracked. I'll have to tighten
NOUN

up your _____ and check.
PLURAL NOUN

GIRL: All right. But make sure you don't scratch my _____
NOUN

or _____ my floor.
VERB

MAD LIBS® is fun to play with friends, but you can also play it by yourself! To begin with, DO NOT look at the story on the page below. Fill in the blanks on this page with the words called for. Then, using the words you have selected, fill in the blank spaces in the story.

Now you've created your own hilarious MAD LIBS® game!

PILOT TO PASSENGERS

_____ ADJECTIVE

_____ CELEBRITY

_____ NOUN

_____ ADJECTIVE

_____ VERB ENDING IN "ING"

_____ PLACE

_____ NUMBER

_____ NUMBER

_____ TYPE OF LIQUID

_____ ADJECTIVE

_____ NOUN

_____ VERB

_____ ADJECTIVE

_____ NOUN

_____ ADJECTIVE

_____ VERB

_____ ADJECTIVE

_____ ADJECTIVE

MAD LIBS®
PILOT TO PASSENGERS

Ladies and gentlemen, welcome aboard _____ Airline's
_{ADJECTIVE}

Flight 750. This is your captain and pilot, _____ . The
_{CELEBRITY}

plane you are traveling on is the latest Strato-_____ , with
_{NOUN}

four _____ engines. At present, we are _____
_{ADJECTIVE}   _{VERB ENDING IN "ING"}

directly over _____ . Our speed is _____ miles per
_{PLACE}   _{NUMBER}

hour, and we are flying at an altitude of _____ feet. If you care
_{NUMBER}

for a cup of _____ or a/an _____ sandwich,
_{TYPE OF LIQUID}   _{ADJECTIVE}

please push the _____ located over your seat, and our
_{NOUN}

flight attendant will be glad to _____ you. We have a/an
_{VERB}

_____ tailwind and will soon by flying through a heavy
_{ADJECTIVE}

_____ storm. So I'll have to ask you all to fasten your _____-
_{NOUN}   _{ADJECTIVE}

belts and _____ your trays to the _____ position. In
_{VERB}   _{ADJECTIVE}

the meantime, I hope you have a/an _____ trip.
_{ADJECTIVE}

MAD LIBS® is fun to play with friends, but you can also play it by yourself! To begin with, **DO NOT** look at the story on the page below. Fill in the blanks on this page with the words called for. Then, using the words you have selected, fill in the blank spaces in the story.

Now you've created your own hilarious MAD LIBS® game!

YUPPIES

NOUN _____

NUMBER _____

ADJECTIVE _____

VERB (PAST TENSE) _____

ADVERB _____

ADJECTIVE _____

VERB _____

ADJECTIVE _____

ADJECTIVE _____

NOUN _____

TYPE OF LIQUID _____

ADJECTIVE _____

ADJECTIVE _____

PLURAL NOUN _____

PLURAL NOUN _____

MAD LIBS
YUPPIES

Yuppies are also called _____ Boomers. They were
NOUN

born after World War _____ . You can identify them by their
NUMBER

_____ hair, _____ skirts, and _____
ADJECTIVE   VERB (PAST TENSE)   ADVERB

_____ shoes. They are _____ -aholics, make lots
ADJECTIVE   VERB

of money, and have _____ taste. They dine at the most
ADJECTIVE

_____ restaurants, eat fresh _____ (formerly
ADJECTIVE   NOUN

known as spaghetti), and always order mineral _____ . They
TYPE OF LIQUID

all sport glasses, even if they have _____ vision. They know
ADJECTIVE

a little about everything, and so tend to have _____ taste.
ADJECTIVE

Yuppies are really just hippies that decided it was better to make

_____ , not _____ .
PLURAL NOUN   PLURAL NOUN

From SOOPER DOOPER MAD LIBS® • Copyright © 2001, 1988 by Price Stern Sloan,
an imprint of Penguin Group (USA) Inc., 345 Hudson Street, New York, NY 10014.

MAD LIBS® is fun to play with friends, but you can also play it by yourself! To begin with, DO NOT look at the story on the page below. Fill in the blanks on this page with the words called for. Then, using the words you have selected, fill in the blank spaces in the story.

Now you've created your own hilarious MAD LIBS® game!

FOOTBALL BROADCAST

ANIMAL (PLURAL)_____

PLURAL NOUN_____

NOUN_____

CELEBRITY (MALE)_____

NOUN_____

PART OF THE BODY_____

NUMBER_____

ANOTHER CELEBRITY_____

ADJECTIVE_____

ANOTHER CELEBRITY (MALE)_____

ADJECTIVE_____

NOUN_____

NOUN_____

VERB ENDING IN "ING"_____

MAD LIBS®
FOOTBALL BROADCAST

Good afternoon, ladies and gentlemen. This is your favorite sports-

caster bringing you the big football game between the Columbia

University _____ and the West Point _____.
                ANIMAL (PLURAL)   PLURAL NOUN

The center has just snapped the _____ back to the Columbia
                                      NOUN

star halfback, _____, who is running around his own left
                CELEBRITY (MALE)

_____. There he's tackled hard around the _____. Now
   NOUN   PART OF THE BODY

it's West Point's ball and _____ to go. They're coming out of the
                              NUMBER

huddle. The ball is snapped back to _____, who fades
                                      ANOTHER CELEBRITY

back and throws a long, _____ pass which is caught by
                              ADJECTIVE

_____, who is West Point's _____ quarterback.
ANOTHER CELEBRITY (MALE)   ADJECTIVE

He's in the clear, and he races over the _____ for a touchdown.
                                            NOUN

No, no, wait! The referee is calling the play back to the 35-_____
                                                              NOUN

line. He's going to penalize West Point for _____.
                                            VERB ENDING IN "ING"

From SOOPER DOOPER MAD LIBS® • Copyright © 2001, 1988 by Price Stern Sloan,
an imprint of Penguin Group (USA) Inc., 345 Hudson Street, New York, NY 10014.